SOME OLD CORNISH FOLK

By SALOME HOCKING

with an Introduction by Amy Ha...

k

1903

© Cornish Hillside Publications, St. Austell PL25 4DW
Printed and bound by
Short Run Press Ltd, Exeter, Devon, EX2 7LW

INTRODUCTION TO THE REPRINTED EDITION
by Dr. Amy Hale

It might be easy at first glance to dismiss Salome Hocking's Some Old Cornish Folk as an idiosyncratic collection of anecdotes and remembrances of village characters, dotted with outdated observations about Cornwall's past. However, this text is, in fact, a valuable record of Cornish lifeways and attitudes from the turn of the twentieth century. It is significant that this book is being re-released now, almost a century after it was originally published. The text helps draw attention to the wider debates about the substance of Cornish identity and culture that have been central to Cornish Studies over the past decade or so. There is no doubt that Some Old Cornish Folk represents a very particular picture of industrial Cornwall.

Hocking's observations are a unique historical contribution to ethnographic practice in Cornwall. During the era in which she was writing, there was a great deal of scholarly focus on antiquities and folklore, trying to capture and reconstruct the customs and beliefs of a pre-industrial Cornwall which was long gone. Hocking, however, wrote about a broadly contemporary Cornwall during a period of change. The text is written by a cultural insider, displaying what anthropologists would call an emic perspective, and so Hocking portrays the Cornish with a sympathy and accuracy borne from intimacy. This sympathy allows her to reveal, perhaps, some of the more painful truths about living a Cornish reality during this difficult period of the territory's history. Her sense of perspective and knack for detail keeps this from being a collection of simple vignettes. Ethnography may have only been partially or secondarily Hocking's intent, but Some Old Cornish Folk remains as a worthwhile account of the Cornish people through a study of individuals and communities.

In many ways Salome Hocking was from a fairly typical Cornish background, yet she led a truly uncommon life. She was born in 1859, just as most of the Cornish economy was undergoing a remarkable transformation as a result of the demise of hard rock mining. Her father was a mining Captain, and she herself grew up in the mining trade, knowing how to process and dress tin. After her family made a transition to farm work, Salome injured her spine in a farm accident which profoundly affected her psychologically and physically. She supported her writing career by teaching in Coombe near St.Stephen-in-Brannel. Salome was also involved in the Methodist chapel in the village as organist and singer in the chapel quartet, which may explain some of her continual return to Methodist musical traditions as a point of reference in Some Old Cornish Folk.

However, despite this rather traditional Cornish upbringing, as she grew older Salome became much more radical. Of course, her successes as a female author during the Victorian period were quite remarkable in themselves. She was obviously a quite prolific writer and by her late twenties had written five novels, most notably Norah

Lang: The Mine Girl (1886). Although it could be interpreted that Salome was riding on the successes of her brothers Silas and Joseph who were also producing copious amounts of moral fiction, as Alan M. Kent argues in his recent comprehensive study of their careers, Pulp Methodism: The Lives and Literature of Silas, Joseph and Salome Hocking, Salome was importantly introducing a woman's perspective into this traditionally male dominated industrial society, where women's voices have been few and far between.

In 1894, Salome married the wealthy publisher Arthur C. Fifield. Her marriage and newfound social mobility introduced her to a variety of new and progressive concepts, which in many ways seemed like a logical, albeit radical progression of her liberal Methodist foundation. Salome became involved with the Utopian Tolstoyan Whiteway community, which advocated 'free union' rather than marriage, and communal property. Her experiences at Whiteway fostered two more novels, which commented on Utopian themes, Beginnings (n.d.) and Belinda the Backward: A Romance of Modern Idealism (1905). Some Old Cornish Folk was originally published in 1903. It is clear from the text that in addition to wanting to record Cornish people, values and voices, that an additional motivation for the piece, was to provide a personal counterpoint to her experiences outside Cornwall.

The bulk of Some Old Cornish Folk is dedicated to short tales of notable characters from her village and family. Hocking succeeds in preserving the stories of remarkable, yet 'everyday' individuals who otherwise may have been lost from the historical record. Many of the cultural features Hocking focuses on could today almost be considered unflattering stereotypes of the Cornish; thrift, poverty, churlishness and severity. Others are quite noble; devoutly religious, dedicated and hard working. Many of her tales are bittersweet, and border on tragic. Hocking's folk generally are not the prettiest of people. Take for instance her first tale of the Little Shoemaker, Elias Polkinhorne. She portrays a small, bad tempered man, clearly physically challenged by a spinal ailment, whose endearing qualities were that he was nosey and bitter! She recounts his unusual love of funerals, and his sometimes unforgiving manner with humour, but notes that he ended his days unloved and alone. Many of Hocking's folk were sturdy and devout, and like the Methodist fiction she wrote, we can only hope that the people she captured went on to a greater reward, as this life proved to be a hard one. Some Old Cornish Folk is valuable because it provides a detailed window into a time and a place which is now past, and we can read this text for historical evidence of artifacts and values. Her literary style of rendering of that work space provides us with what anthropologists would call 'thick description', providing us with details and atmosphere that we readers can use to further understand the Cornwall of her time. For example, her depiction of Polkinhorne's cobbler's shop provides us with a vivid picture of a trade which has passed away. The high backed seats in the dark waiting area, the wax-topped crocks of water, and the instruments for stretching leather which were so much a part of Salome's era and community are no longer a part of our own. Her descriptions of buildings and spaces are particularly of interest. We can see what a chapel looked like before electric lighting, how the pews were organized and what people wore, and we can treat this as a reliable record.

Almost more interesting, though, is Hocking's portrayal of customs and values that the Cornish held during the turn of the twentieth century. These aspects of culture are often the hardest to depict, and her status as 'cultural insider' lends weight to the accuracy of the description. Hocking's Cornwall is industrial, Methodist and poor. Some of the more interesting details concern values and customs surrounding Methodism and the chapel's centrality to the community at the time which she was writing. It seems clear that although Methodism carried a spiritual message which resonated uniquely with this industrial society, Methodism also shaped social interactions and Cornish style. Of course she refers to customs such as the tea treat and the Cornish love of singing, but she also captures more complex aspects of Cornish value systems.

For instance, in more than one incident, Hocking shows us that the Cornish of this period valued verbal acuity and cleverness. Although toward the end of the book she refers to the Cornish trait of being sparse with words, and using carefully constructed phrases (in opposition to the more wordy Cockney, who she often uses as a cultural foil to the Cornish), she records that chapel goers would be rapt in attention at a sermon which was well delivered, but very critical of one which was not. The key to a successful sermon seemed to be performance style rather than the message itself. It is through these types of details that we can start to appreciate Hocking's skill as a cultural observer, and to understand the depth of the Cornish values that she articulated.

Hocking makes it clear that the Cornwall she is recording is a Cornwall that is soon passing, yet she does not spend much time speculating about what Cornwall will become. The book is nostalgic, but it is not mournful. She remembers and records, but her main purpose is to confidently celebrate the uniqueness of the Cornish spirit. The occasional romantic references to the 'quaint' and the picturesque should be read more as the musings of a proud Cornishwoman. Her bias and love of her own country in no way alter the important contribution of this work to enhancing our understanding of the development of Cornish culture.

Amy Hale

Dr Amy Hale was born in Michigan and is a Folklorist and Anthropologist. She is presently a Visiting Professor of Mythology at the University of Central Florida and former Lecturer in Contemporary Celtic Studies at the Institute of Cornish Studies, University of Exeter. She is co-editor of New Directions in Celtic Studies and Inside Merlin's Cave: A Cornish Arthurian Reader 1000-2000. Other recent publications have included chapters in Celtic Geographies: Old Culture, New Times and Cornish Studies.

CONTENTS

THE . . . .
LITTLE . . .
SHOEMAKER

I

The Little Shoemaker

T was not until some years after I had left Cornwall that I quite realised how quaint were some of the characters whom I had known from infancy, and how rare they are now becoming. The younger race, though still retaining the Cornish vernacular and many of the old customs, presents fewer interesting personal traits. It would take the pen of a George Eliot or a Thomas Hardy to do these old folk justice, and I am more than half afraid, labour of love though it is to me, that my photographs will be but blurred and incomplete; but if they serve to recall "zum ov the ould people" to the minds of the many Cornish men and women who have left their

9

native county, I shall be content. For in some small way I shall have rescued those dear old people from oblivion, if only for a short time.

As I look back, not one stands out plainer in my memory than Elias Polkinhorne, the shoemaker. He was a queer little old man, not more than 3 ft. 10 in., with a short, round face fringed with stiff, grey whiskers. He had a wide mouth, and a full set of very large yellow teeth; his nose, too, was large, with a big wart on the tip. He wore his hair very long, and on his head was always an old felt hat, known as a billycock, originally black, but now rusty with age and dust. The brim rested on his ears, but on windy days, for further security, the hat was tied underneath his chin with a piece of cord. He had a very large hump on his back, which was a constant source of interest to us children, as was also the wart on his nose, and a large birth-mark on his hand, somewhat resembling a strawberry. I don't remember that we ever thought him ugly, or even plain. We considered him queer, and sometimes he was very cross; but, somehow, snarl at us as he would, he could not keep us away. He and his

quaint old shop quite compensated for wet
Saturdays, our weekly holiday. How the poor
old man would fume when one after another
we insinuated ourselves into his dark shop ; but
how boldly we lifted the latch when we had
a little job of mending to do, and with what
an "I've-got-the-right" kind of air we seated
ourselves on the vacant seat (provided the
journeyman was not there) by the bench, and
turned over the miscellaneous assortment of
nails, bits of leather, pieces of glass, waxed
ends, hammers, pincers, and all the other de-
lightful things that are t o be found in a real,
proper shoemaker's shop.

The shop was as much a source of interest
to us as its master, and came in for a share of
our admiring attentions. The walls were built of
cob ; and when the old man's back was turned,
we used to enjoy scratching with a nail, and
seeing the dust trickle down. The roof was
thatched, and we liked to look up at the places
where it had bulged in, and wonder how many
more coats of thatch those bent rafters would
stand without breaking. But this was only on
sunshiny days, when the door and hatch were both

open; then we had a fine view of the black
rafters, and the hundreds of spiders' webs
that hung in festoons in all directions. What
a glorious time the spiders must have had
there, for they had never been disturbed since
the place was built. But on dull or wet days we
could see nothing but general blackness, which
extended also to the back of the shop. There
was only one window, and that, what with dust,
cobwebs, and the smallness of the panes, only
served to throw a little light on the bench be-
neath, and as far back as the old, high-backed
settle, where customers sat when they wanted
to be measured, and old chums rested when
they came in for a chat. Behind that settle was
unexplored ground to us; for though we had
sometimes peeped around and looked with
curious eyes at the black crocks of water with
pieces of wax swimming on top, we had never
ventured, with one exception, to go behind.
This was not altogether surprising; for one had
to walk warily on that old mud floor, with
pits in some places large enough to bury a
cat, and muddy shoes and leggings waiting
to be mended scattered in all directions. I

remember one large pit just inside the door,
which after a heavy rain was filled with water ;
for the shop stood on much lower ground than
the road outside, from which you descended by
three stone steps. It was always a matter of
great interest to us to watch an unsuspecting
customer enter the shop at such times, and I
think even old Elias, in his grim way, used to
enjoy their meeting with the unexpected. I
am afraid our mothers would have thought the
language used by the unregenerate not quite
fit for our innocent ears.

The exception mentioned just now was a
rather inquisitive boy whom we named Hunkey ;
I don't remember why. Once he really went
behind the settle, but quickly returned, and
immediately rushed out of the shop. Of course
we followed him, and at last extracted the
startling information that he had seen the
devil. Further questioned, he had seen something standing by the wall, all black, and
tremendously big, with two great shining eyes.
We believed this for some time, and then some
one suggested that it might only have been a
piece of harness with brass plates, hung on a

roll of leather. This was very commonplace, but it would be such a relief to believe it (for somehow we did not relish the idea of being shut up with his Satanic Majesty), that we decided to accept this explanation, and then we all rounded on Hunkey, and laughed at him for being in such a fright. But, all the same, at the bottom we respected him, for he was really the only one who had ever ventured behind the settle.

When Elias was in a good temper, and we had any little piece of news to tell him—and we were veritable gossips in that respect—we managed to have quite a comfortable time. And what bland courtiers we developed into, to be sure—doing our best to flatter the old man and to make him laugh. Nothing pleased him better than to hear of any new developments in the " courting " world ; he would grunt, and show his yellow teeth with such evident appreciation, that it always inspired us to fresh efforts. Once I remember, as a last resource to retain our footing, I told him that a certain young gentleman was in the habit of calling at our house very often, and that I believed he was

" sweet " on my sister. Never shall I forget Laura's vexation when the old man accosted her on her way home from church, and, with one of his funny grunts, said, " Uh, uh! where's yer new zidemaate, then? " As the youthful swain had not yet declared himself, this was very embarrassing, especially as it was supposed to be a secret, known only to the members of our own family. I trembled, for fear that my agency in the matter should be known; but the old man was loyal. Afterwards, when I grew to a marriageable age, the old man's curiosity in such matters had not abated, and I was often asked why I did not get a " zidemaate," and when I replied, as did another little maid, " No one asked me, sir," he would shake his head unbelievingly, and grunt, " Uh, uh! too 'teckler, I reckon—too 'teckler."

But to come back. Sometimes we had no news; and when we tried to suppose some, the old man was too keen for us, and all our blandishments were met with snarls, and we were uncompromisingly ordered off. Hard words we bore bravely; but when Elias got off his stool and threatened us with that, we thought his language rather too personal, and departed sadly for other pastures.

Poor old Elias was a bachelor ; but it was reported that once in his middle-aged days he had set his heart on a tall, bouncing girl of twenty, and she, thinking of the wealth which he was always supposed to possess, had partly accepted him. The old man gave up his lodgings and took a house, and even went to the extravagance of buying a quart of honey: it was three shillings a quart, too. " To sweeten 'er when she gits in a bad temper," he explained. But the wedding never came off. The fair one altered her mind, and married a younger man. This was Elias's only matrimonial venture, and it probably accounted for the many cynical remarks he used to make about the foolishness of young people getting married. Once, when my mother hinted to him that he would be a happier man if he had a wife and children, the old man sadly assented, and further remarked that, if he had his time to go over again, he would not live such a lonely life. But as a rule he never talked of himself.

I never knew what were the old man's

religious beliefs. He was a due attendant at chapel, and listened very attentively to the the sermon, but he never allied himself to the church; he was a member of the congregation only, and always sat in the " free seats." He favoured those preachers most who were fluent; but if a local brother had what the old man termed a "tight jacket," great was his glee, and many caustic remarks would be made to his customers the next day. If a sermon had nothing but its fluency to recommend it, he would remark, "A pud [pretty] li'le taale, but no beef in it."

Once or twice an evangelist having more time on his hands than the regular ministers, who lived several miles away from our village, called at Elias's shop, and tried to have some serious talk, but the old man was non-committal. A few grunts and a tremendous hammering of nails would be his only reply, and he was generally considered hopeless.

He was a peculiar little figure at all times; but on a dark night, with his bent back emphasised by a black bag of " uppers " slung over his shoulders, which he was taking home from the

2

station, his little black form looked rather
ghoulish, and I was always glad to respond
to the old man's " Ebbnin " (" Good-evening ").
Usually he walked fast, with short, jerky steps ;
but on Sundays, when his top lip was shaven and
his hair trimmed a little—he was his own barber,
and not at all particular about the cut, one side
being often longer than the other—and he had
his Sunday clothes on, he walked more leisurely,
with his hands put back under his coat, and
his fingers twiddling the tail.   When in a good
temper, he kept up a cheerful kind of noise that
was not exactly a whistle, for it had only two
notes. I have heard women make a similar
noise when trying to whistle.

The old man seemed to take a melancholy
pleasure in attending funerals, and his funny
little form might generally be seen on the out-
skirts of the crowd. Going home, if he fell in
with congenial company, his face would relax,
and he would remark, jocularly, " So poor old
—— es teeled [tilled] in at laast. Dedn think
'ee wud 'ave gone off so soon ; thought 'ee wud
'ave chated the sex'on this winter."

Sometimes, on a cold day, Elias would indulge

in a glass of grog. He was not given to tippling, and it was seldom that he indulged, save at funerals, or on tithe-paying days, which meant wearing his Sunday clothes and a half-holiday.

I remember being once convulsed after a funeral at the sight of the old man zigzagging down a lane at full speed. He evidently wanted to keep clear of the ditches, but they seemed to have a fatal fascination for him, for he no sooner got out of one than he found himself in the other. He was going at such a furious rate that I had a difficulty in dodging him, and I know as I watched him out of sight I laughed until the tears ran down my cheeks. Usually the sight of a drunken man saddens me; but Elias looked so comical, and so bent on getting home in the shortest time, and by the longest route, that only the ludicrous side of the thing struck me.

Elias could not be considered a " neat " shoemaker, but his boots were always strong, and much better worth the money than any I have bought since. He was not considered a generous man, and I never remember his giving me anything for the missionaries—as I wanted

to secure the two-shilling book reward, I daresay I badgered him sufficiently—and he seldom
gave anything to a collection; but he was
always just and straightforward in all his
dealings. He never forgave an injury, and I
never heard of his doing one. He appreciated
kindness, and returned it in his own peculiar
way. As a mark of special favour, he called on
his few friends when they were sick, but never
at any other time, save on business. Sunday
was the day he chose for these friendly calls,
and before leaving, by way of a bit of pleasantry,
he would ask the sick man if he was " mose
ready to be teeled in," or if he meant to " chate
the sex'on."

When at last the grim visitor knocked at
poor old Elias's door, there was no one to bid
him enter, and no one to wish the old man God-
speed through the valley; for he died as he had
lived—lonely and uncared for.

AUNT
BETTY

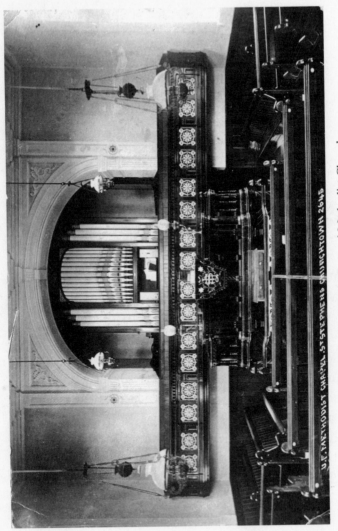

Interior St. Stephen-in-Brannel Methodist Chapel

II

Aunt Betty

UNT BETTY ROWSE was re-markable chiefly for her smallness of stature and her great fluency of speech in the class and prayer meeting. She was almost a dwarf, but never seemed to be conscious of the fact; and, indeed, her size was apt to be deceptive, as it was of a varying quantity. Most people have their clothes made to fit them, and many are the heart-burnings suffered when they don't; but Aunt Betty was saved all this trouble, for she made herself fit her clothes. Hence it was not at all surprising to see her very stout one Sunday and almost slim the next. Her size depended entirely on the size of the person whose dress or jacket she wore. Nobody ever saw Aunt Betty

with a new dress on ; for her income, which she
received from the parish, and which amounted
to half a crown a week, would not support such
extravagance. But, spite of that, she was
always decently dressed, the members of the
chapel she attended remembering her when they
had a dress that had grown old fashioned. The
antiquity of a dress never seemed to trouble
Aunt Betty ; for she kept her eyes open, and
generally managed to make sufficient altera-
tions to give her dresses a slight flavour of
up-to-dateness.

I have since thought that Aunt Betty's eloquence was not quite so favourably received at
the chapel as it might have been; for when,
as sometimes happened, there was a gap in
the prayer meeting, several " brothers " having
been called on without response, and the silence growing painful, there was always a tone
of misgiving in the prayer-leader's hesitating
" Sister Rowse," and it was generally followed
by a slight snigger from the back of the chapel,
where the sinners were wont to congregate.
But the heads of all the " youngsters " would
be raised in delighted expectation. How we

enjoyed seeing her straighten herself up, and
then deliberately turn round and kneel upon
her pew with her face towards the congregation!
What a weight of responsibility seemed to rest
on her, as she prayed for us all, that we might
be snatched as "bran's from the burnin',"
and that our lives might become as "bright as
the stars in the farmament"! How her voice
rose and fell and swelled out in such sonorous
tones that we wondered where they came from!
But we wondered more, as the minutes went by,
when she was going to stop. We understood
then why the prayer-leader hesitated before
he loosed those flood-gates of eloquence. Aunt
Betty's prayers were not so much petitions as
general exhortations. She would begin by
lowering us all to the level of "grovellin'
worms," "onworthy dust," and "filthy rags";
and then, as the enormity of our sins seemed to
grow on her, she would pray that the "Lord
would strike as with a 'ammer our flinty 'earts,
and breek our 'earts of stone." How solemn
her voice grew as she spoke of those who ran
with the "giddy multitude to do evul," and
who, instead of being as a "sweet saaver in

the 'ouse of Hisrael, were full of wounds and brooses and pootrifyin' sores"! Although we always anticipated Aunt Betty's prayers with a certain amount of glee, we were entirely subdued by the time she had finished. If she went on *too* long, we used to create a diversion by upsetting the " crickets " (small wooden footstools); and as the floor was of lime-ash, they made considerable noise. But this was rather a risky business; and if the culprit was discovered, he or she was apt to regret it as soon as the service was over.

It was not often that I was allowed to sit with the other children. My mother generally liked to have me near her, where she could keep her eye on me; but if we happened to be early, and she stopped outside to speak to other early comers, I always slid into chapel, and ensconced myself in the big, square pew on the left, which was originally intended for the choir; but as there never was one in those days, it was claimed by the children. I liked to sit facing the congregation, and with my back to my mother, who sat in the pew nearest the pulpit. Under those circumstances chapel was quite bearable. It was so nice to look all round and see what everybody was doing. I always waited with interest to see Granfer Pearce settle himself back in his pew with his red silk handkerchief thrown over his head to keep off the draughts, while grandma at his side closed her eyes, so that she might hear better. I waited anxiously, too, for Uncle Abraham to scratch his throat and then expectorate on the floor; for then we knew that he was growing sleepy, and soon his head would fall back, and his toothless mouth would open, and then we held our breaths while Nipper, one of the boys, seized the opportunity when none of the elders were looking to aim a paper pellet at this open cavern. He seldom missed, and Uncle Abraham's look of horror when he woke up gasping and choking over this obstruction was worth a good deal to us.

Then there was Mr. Thomas, who always slept through the sermon, but who invariably drew his hand down over his face when it was ended, with a reverent " Praise the Lord," as if he had only been meditating. Then there was Mrs. Roberts, who generally came in late, but who always turned round in her pew, bowed her head slightly, put three fingers in front of her mouth, took a good look all round to see who were there, and how they were dressed, and then sat down, no doubt satisfied that she had done the correct thing. After all this there was the chapel to be looked at, and the hats counted, which hung on pegs against the white-washed walls. There were four windows in the chapel—two on the right, one on the left, and one in the end behind the pulpit. From one on the right I could see any people who might be passing on the road outside, and on the left the cows grazing in the field. Some-times they came and looked in, as if wondering what we were doing. The chapel was built on a bit of waste ground by the roadside, and was a low thatched building with thick cob walls. When the shutters were up, it was often mis-taken by strangers for a cattle-house. Internally it has been greatly altered since the days of which I write ; there are several new pews with wood flooring, a rostrum instead of the old pulpit, lamps instead of candles, and a har-monium to lead the singing. But I like best to

think of it as I first knew it, with the funny
little old pulpit painted blue and red, and the
candle-box hung by the side of the stairs, and
the faded red moreen covering on the bookstand,
and the clumsily carved pieces of worm-eaten
wood which held the candles. We always held
our breath when the preacher caught hold of
one of those pieces of wood; but nothing ever
happened, except that sometimes in snuffing
the candle he snuffed it out. There were two
wooden chandeliers, carved in an original fashion,
and painted to match the pulpit, and holding
three candles apiece. There were two other
candles stuck on tall, upright pieces of wood on
each side of the leaders' pews, so that altogether
there was quite an illumination.

The part of the service which I liked best of
all was the singing. There was always such an
element of uncertainty about it, as when someone would raise a short-metre tune to a long-
metre hymn. We did our best to make the
words fit; but Granfer Pearce, who sang bass,
would stop with a snort of disapproval, and say
in a loud whisper, " You've got the wrong tewn."
I have known as many as three tunes to be

started before it came right; and then Granfer, in his exasperation at such stupidity, would raise the tune in a loud, rasping treble, jerking out the words as if they were his enemies, and he wanted to annihilate them; but he could not keep this up for long, and quickly dropped back to his bass. Once I remember him raising a tune which no one seemed to know; but, with my usual audacity and desire to help, I assisted Granfer in singing the treble. We got on well during the first verse, for I watched him, and could see by the way his head wagged whether the tune was going up or down; but in the second verse, after giving me the start, Granfer returned to his bass. Then I was in a dilemma. However, I did my best, and kept on bravely, though in rather an uncertain voice, making the tune suit the words, and harmonizing as well as I could with Granfer's bass; but never shall I forget the withering look he cast on me as he again broke raspingly into treble, and I knew that my well-meant efforts were a failure, and retired sadly from the contest, allowing Granfer to bear the brunt of the battle alone. At the end of the third verse he shut his book with a bang, and said to the preacher in an angry, impressive way, " You must dasist, fer my voice is awl gone."

But those times were only the exceptions. When they hit on good congregational tunes, we all joined in heartily ; and this being the only part of the service in which the children could assist without being reproved, we made the most of our opportunity. Many a time at the end of a verse have I seen Granfer Pearce look across at us with a beaming smile on his big, ruddy face, and heard him murmur tenderly, " Little dears." The greatest fault which could be found with the singing at our chapel was the time. We were given to singing slowly, spite of Granfer Pearce's efforts to pull us along ; but Uncle Tom Martin sang at racing speed, and always finished the verse by the time we had got half-way through. He bore us no malice though, for he invariably came back and helped us out, and always managed to finish then before we did.

But I must not forget Aunt Betty, for there was no one in the chapel who could get up

" higher " than she could,—and we got up
pretty high sometimes, for those old tunes often
ran up to A ; and when, as was often the case,
the tune was raised a note too high, it was no
easy work to clear those top notes successfully.
But here was where Aunt Betty shone. No
matter how high the tune ascended, Aunt
Betty's voice could always be heard above all
the others. We often stopped singing to watch
her. She would throw back her little round
head covered with a high-bowed black bonnet,
and, with her chin elevated, emit such shrill
screams as caused Granfer Pearce himself to
stop singing and turn round and glower at her.
Once he was heard to remark to his wife,
" Why, the little crettur must be *vull* of noise ! "
But nothing deterred Aunt Betty, and she would
wipe the perspiration off her face, loosen her
bonnet-strings during the reading of the next
verse, and then burst forth again with renewed
vigour.

Aunt Betty was always a due attendant at
the chapel; and although she was only in receipt
of parish pay, yet she never missed putting a
penny in the collecting-box (luckily for her, they

only made collections once a month) or paying
a shilling a quarter for her ticket. To do this
the poor old soul often went without butter,
and boiled her tea leaves two or three times
over. Yet she seldom complained, and was
nearly always cheerful. Sometimes, when speaking of her husband, who had been dead for
many years, she would shed a few tears, but I
think it was more out of pity for her own lone-
liness than because she regretted him. From all
accounts he had been a big, lazy, shiftless kind
of man, and Aunt Betty had not "set much
store by him." It was not often that she ever
went to a chapel tea, for she could not afford
the necessary eightpence; and although they
would have given her a ticket, Aunt Betty was
too proud to accept it. Once or twice some
kind friend sent the money to pay for her tea
privately. Then it was good to see the little
creature march up boldly to the ticket-seller,
and lay down her money. To her a tea-meeting
was a great excitement; and though she seemed
to enjoy herself immensely, yet it was generally
followed, she once told my mother, by a sleep-
less night. She liked best, however, to go to

our annual school tea, or "treat," as it was
called. Aunt Betty was generally among the
first arrivals; for then, as the notices put it,
"we form into procession, and, headed by a
brass band, perambulate the village and the
adjoining neighbourhood, returning to the field
kindly lent for the occasion by Mr. So-and-So,
where later on we shall be regaled with tea and
cake." I never knew the wording of this notice
to be altered; but I think it was original with
our school, for once a local brother from
another parish in reading the notice stumbled
over the long words, and informed us that
we should "peeramble the village, and afterwards be *regalled* with tay and caake." He
further added by way of comment that
he "'adn't a doubt that all the wemmen
would turn up, fer they allays flocked around
a tay-pot."

It was amusing to see Aunt Betty's little, short,
black-garbed figure, between two long-legged,
short-frocked girls, walking behind the band.
Aunt Betty did not attempt all the "perambu-
lations"; she only walked round the village,
joining us later when we entered the field.

She was as young as any of us that day, and would, I verily believe, have run races for nuts, if her breath had permitted. She was very fond of the band, and generally seated herself on the shafts of the waggon—which formed the band-stand—and kept time with both head and feet. It spoke well for Aunt Betty's ears that she could sit so near, for our local band was more noted for its strength than its sweetness. It was cheap, however; for we paid ten shillings less than we should have had to pay for the prize band from the adjoining parish, while we listened to a great deal more music (?)—and we liked plenty for our money. Sometimes, to increase its strength, the band would hire a famous drummer from the next parish. He was a very little man, with black hair whiskers nearly covering his face, big bushy eyebrows, and small black eyes. When he walked behind the big drum, nothing was to be seen of him in front save his face; but that was worth seeing, for with every stroke on the drum his face made an accompanying contortion. When he beat with his right hand, his mouth went up towards his left eye, and *vice versa*; but when

he made a final flourish with both hands, both
sides of his face, mouth, and eyes worked
accordingly. He was a most enthusiastic
drummer, and the tale was told that he used
to dream about it at nights, and once when
dreaming that he was playing a quick battle
march broke three of his wife's ribs. After
that it was remarked that she hated the name
of war, and believed in peace at any price.
I cannot vouch for the truth of this story,
although it was always related as a fact ; but
we were not given to verifying statements—if
a story was a good one, we were content to
take it on its merits.

Aunt Betty did not spend all her time with
the band, for there were the " stannings "
(sweet stalls) to be inspected, and she was not
above sampling their contents when anyone
offered to treat her. Once we thought that
Aunt Betty was going to change her name, for
a certain lame man had been seen treating her
to a pound of " comforts " (comfits) ; and as they
cost two shillings, this was thought significant,
especially when a little later Aunt Betty was
seen wearing a red turnover (small shawl)

instead of her jacket. But it came to nothing, as do so many other flirtations.

Although Aunt Betty was humble and deferential to those she considered her superiors, yet when asked for an opinion she gave it in quite an authoritative way, and on some subjects, mostly religious, she held very strong views. Once, because of something being done of which she had disapproved, she stayed away from the chapel for quite six months. The poor old soul must have found that it was a losing game; for when it was known that no amount of persuasion or argument would turn her, she was left severely alone. She must have missed the baskets of odds and ends of food which before had been such an addition to her parish pay; for when winter came on, Aunt Betty quietly returned; but whether she had changed her opinion or only held it in abeyance, was known to herself alone.

When I grew older, Aunt Betty's religion seemed to me a rather poor and narrow conception; but she found it all-sufficient, and believed in it with all her heart. It stood the test too; for once when she was thought to be near the Jordan, she had no fear of the last enemy, and told her friends that " Jesus was precious"; but she recovered, and by latest accounts she is still alive. I don't think she will ever see this, for she reads little save her Bible and Wesley's hymns; but even if she did, she would not recognise herself, for it has not been given to her to see herself as others see her.

**SEBUDAH
AND** . .
AARON .

III

Sebudah and Aaron

Y earliest recollection of Sebudah Wakeham was at a pig-weighing scene. There was a good deal of ambition in our village as to who should rear and feed the finest pig; hence it was not at all uncommon, when one was killed, for the neighbours to call and inspect the animal, and pass opinions as to its probable weight.

I daresay I had known Sebudah at a much earlier period, but my memory carries no record of the knowledge.

The pig in question was the property of Aaron and Sebudah Wakeham, although, as Sebudah had fed and talked to it three times a day since its birth, it is very probable that she considered it peculiarly her own. The pig was hung from its hind legs in Sebudah's kitchen, with a potato in its mouth, which, could piggy have known it, would have seemed a bitter piece of irony, for in life he had never had all the potatoes his nature craved for. But, be this as it may, he was thickly larded, and altogether was a fine specimen, and did Sebudah credit, although Sirree Nick, who prided himself on feeding the heaviest pigs in the village, was heard to remark in a low tone, " Ef the pig 'ad bin 'is, he shud 'ave gived un another bushell ov bairley."

After the pig had been thoroughly inspected, the work of cutting up commenced. The head was taken off, then the remainder halved and quartered, and then followed the weighing, which everybody awaited with much interest. My brother and I were told off to mark down the weight on our slates, and very important I know I felt. When we had, each of us, added up the figures several times, to convince Sebudah that no mistake had been made, we announced that the pig weighed seventeen score six pounds and a half. (We reckoned by twenties in Cornwall.)

" Dedn' think 'ee wud 'ave bin quite s' 'eavy,"
muttered Sirree Nick, in a slightly vexed tone.
" Mine was awnly two pounds 'eavier."

After the pig had been weighed, and before
the " stillyers " (stillyards) had been taken down,
there were several who wanted to try their
weight, Sebudah among the number. She was
a little, thin, lath-like woman, with a face as
ruddy as a winter apple, pretty dark eyes, and
black hair, only slightly streaked with grey,
combed in shining bands down each side of her
face. The young man who weighed Sebudah
so manipulated the weight on the beam as to
make her about forty pounds more than her
usual weight. I can see her now, seated on the
rope, which was looped to a crook on the stillyards, in the shape of a swing, her eyes turned
up towards the beam, and a look of perplexity
on her face.

" I doan't knaw 'ow 'tes, I'm sure," she remarked. " I aan't bin aitin' more'n usual, and
me cloas doan't veel a bit tight. Ax Aaron,
then." Sebudah seldom made a statement
without appealing to Aaron for corroboration.

Aaron, a rather tall, thin, red-whiskered man,

with a bald head and a permanent look of discontent on his face, gave a slight snigger, and said, in his peculiar drawling voice, which was so complete a contrast to Sebudah's quick speech, " 'Ow shud I knaw 'ow much you do ait. I baan't 'ome awl the time. Wemmen can gen'rally do their share when there's anything good to ait about. Iss they can."

This speech was received with such general laughter that Aaron chuckled with pride at his own wit. The real fun of Aaron's speech lay in the fact that about six weeks before someone had asked his son when the pig was to be fed, and he answered, with several winks and sniffs, without which he seemed unable to speak, a peculiarity inherited from his mother, " Ma mother zay we ought to put 'im in to feed next week, or else we shaan't 'ave a bit of vlesh to ait, for it'll taake six weeks to feed un, and she zay she doan't believe we've got more'n a pound 'nd haalf of baacon left." As that pound and a half of bacon represented all the meat they had tasted for six weeks, the reader will understand why Aaron's joke was so much appreciated.

The next scene I have any distinct recollection of is seeing Sebudah and my Aunt Eleanor
seated in our kitchen listening to a thrilling
ghost story, which my mother was relating,
à propos of some strange sight which had been
seen in the neighbourhood. I think it is from
my mother that we have inherited what little
story-telling talent we have. She had a keen
eye for dramatic effect, and knew how to work
up her audience to the proper pitch of excitement, and leave them gasping and shivering at
the climax. I cannot recall the story, which
had been told her by an eye-witness, I believe ;
all that I can remember is the effect produced
on my aunt and Sebudah. Aunt Eleanor's
usually laughing face was clouded with the
nearest approach to a look of horror which her
comely features could assume, and she wrung
her hands and squeezed her lips together as she
gave vent to such expressions as "My dear
cheeld, how very terrible! Why, I believe I
should have died on the spot!"

Sebudah, on the contrary, wore an un-
moved face, but listened with fixed attention,
answering Aunt Eleanor's interjections with

several sniffs and winks, and an occasional "Iss, 'tis queer."

The story could not have impressed her very much, however, for she immediately broke the silence which should have followed this thrilling narrative with a story of her own. I can remember it very easily, because it was so short, and depended so little on the usual accessories of background and staging.

"You knaw Billy Cundy?" she began. "Well, wan night 'ee was comin' 'ome fr'm Grampound, 'nd jist as 'ee was passin' thickey great 'eap ov stoanes in Zugga Lane, 'ee 'eeard the whishtest grooans, 'nd then the stoanes beginned t' rattle down in the roade, 'nd then 'ee 'eeard chains jangling, 'nd he tuk to 'es 'eels." Here she paused, not to note the effect, but to indulge in several winks and sniffs; then, swallowing audibly, she concluded, "'Nd 'twas zaid 'twas the devill, yunnaw."

Aunt Eleanor, who had at first made an attempt to listen seriously to this blood-curdling story, now burst into a merry laugh, and, rubbing her hands, said, gleefully, "Why,

Sebudah, I expect the old gent came up for a bit of fresh air."

Sebudah Wakeham was always spoken of as a very careful, saving wife; and this was no small praise in a county where the majority of poor people are more or less thrifty. Sebudah had a passion for saving. It was utterly impossible for her to waste anything which she considered of any value. Her week-day dresses were patched until you could hardly tell the original material; while her aprons were mere strips with continual darnings. Aaron, on the contrary, was given to sudden bursts of extravagance; and on such occasions he would not only buy clothes for himself, but dresses and bonnets for his wife. He was greatly influenced by Sebudah, however, and it was only when he was away from her that he dared indulge in such dangerous freaks. On one of those occasions he bought Sebudah a new dress of a very vivid light-green shade, and a very high-crowned black bonnet. Sebudah was greatly exercised in her mind over this extravagance, and was only slightly reconciled by being told that the articles were "bargains"; but, submitting to the inevitable, she had the dress made up, and wore it the following Sunday.

In those days most of the middle-aged and elderly women wore dark-coloured clothes, and were seldom seen out of doors without shawls or mantles. I remember what a startling vision Sebudah was when she entered the chapel that Sunday afternoon with the new green dress worn "outdoor fit" (that is, without jacket or shawl). She affected, when spoken to about her grandeur, not to be best pleased with it; and perhaps it was with the intention of toning it down that, save on very fine Sundays, she wore over the famous green a black cloth jacket, trimmed with crêpe, and a crêpe bonnet. Whatever were Sebudah's views on the matter, Aaron's pride in the new costume was very evident. Any fine Sunday afternoon they might be seen wending their way to the chapel, single file, Aaron walking two or three yards behind Sebudah, that he might view the effect, and also reply to her question as to whether her dress was touching the ground. To an ordinary observer this would seem impossible, for she always tucked her dress up under each arm;

but as the skirts were voluminous in those days, a fold might slip from the restraint and touch the dusty road—hence her oft-repeated question to Aaron.

I don't know if Sebudah cared much for the sermons, for she was not a religious woman in the ordinary acceptance of the term. She was rather proud of the fact that she could go to revival services and never "feel anything," though she admitted that this was not always so. "I can mind the time," she would remark, with one of her funny little sniffs, "when I used to veel awful queer in a revival, and I used to cry sometimes, but I never went down" (knelt at the penitent-form), she added, triumphantly; "but that was 'ears ago. I never veel anything now."

When some more-enlightened friend remarked that perhaps she had sinned away her day of grace, she sniffed, and answered, indifferently, "I dunnaw, I'm sure. I spoase I sh'll git converted zome time; but, law, I'm s' busy now, that I aan't got time to go to the services."

When her daughter lay ill, and the doctor had pronounced the case hopeless, Sebudah

4

seemed anxious that she should have some
spiritual consolation, and came running to ask
my mother to allow me to go for a certain
prayer-leader to come and pray with our " Jane
Ann." Mother replied that it was late in the
evening, and she didn't like to send me. This
rather worried Sebudah, and she was turning
away sadly, when a thought seemed to strike
her, and she said, hurriedly, " Cudn *you* come
and pray weth our Jaane Ann ? " adding, by
way of encouragement, " Doan't matter what
you zay, yunnaw."

Aaron was considered more enlightened than
Sebudah, for he could read ; but Sebudah could
neither read nor write. When their only re-
maining child had grown up and left our country,
I had to conduct the correspondence. Sebudah
was not prolific in news ; and when asked what
I must write, her usual reply was, " I dunnaw ;
there edn much news. You c'n tell'n we be
boath well, and ax 'ow 'ee es, 'nd that Aaron
'nd me boath zend love. Doan't we, Aaron ? "

" Iss, to be sure. Purty thing ef we dedn.
Iss, it wud," Aaron would reply.

Further pressed for news, Sebudah would

say, contemplatively, " Well, tell'n that the zow
'ave got nine vears [sucklings]. She 'ad ten,
but she lied top wan, poor lil thing." And
then, her face lighting up and her eyes spark-
ling, she would add, " Iss, and you mus' tell'n
'bout the cats. Curley was 'es, yunnaw. He
naamed un Curley 'cause 'ee car [carry] 'es tail
on 'is back. 'Ere 'ee es : edn 'ee a beauty ? "

" Iss, Daavid used to be very fond of Curley—
iss, 'ee ded," Aar would interject. He seldom
omitted to repeat a remark twice. Perhaps
that was a kind of protest because Sebudah
allowed him so little share in the conversation.
If Aaron commenced to tell anything, Sebudah
invariably interrupted, and told the story in her
own inimitable way, taking not the slightest
notice of Aaron's complaining " Lev me spake
a minute, Sebudah—caan't 'ee ? "

Sometimes he would appear slightly vexed,
and say, sharply, " Howld yer tongue a minute,
caan't 'ee ? " And then he would add, with a
wintry smile, " My wumman waan't lave me
spake." But Sebudah completely ignored all
these interruptions. Once started to talk about
cats, and Sebudah had plenty to tell. They

were very wonderful creatures in her estimation, and she would remark proudly of Prin, a beautiful light tabby, that it "wan't a bit of good to zay ' Puss, puss, puss,' for 'ee doan't knaw nawthin' 'bout that ; but ef you zay ' Pren, Pren, Pren,' he'll run like vre." Then she would add, with a smile in Aaron's direction, " The Prenner es Aaron's cat. He naamed un Pren, but I call un the Prenner."

Sebudah was also very fond of her young pigs, and would tell you little differences in the character of each one. " Do ee zee that little wan weth the spot 'pon 'is ear ? " she would ask, and then add, proudly, " 'Ell ait tetties [potatoes] nearly as vast as 'is mawther. 'Nd do ee zee that wan weth wan ear cocked up ? 'Ee's a nointed [unmanageable] little chap. 'Ee'll screech like a whitneck ef 'ee caan't git boath 'es vit [feet] in the traff [trough]. 'Ere, give et to me, Aaron"—this to Aaron, who had by this time fetched some cabbage leaves to show off their rapid eating powers. But Sebudah would not allow him to feed them, for fear he should give them too large pieces, taking no notice of his " Lev me give it to them, Sebudah."

When the cabbage leaves had been exhausted, as she thought, and Sebudah stooped to pick up her stick, which she kept to enforce order, Aaron seized the opportunity to throw a large piece, which he had hidden behind his back, to the one with the spot on his ear. Sebudah caught sight of it, and cried frantically, " Why, Aaron, you'll chuck [choke] un ! "

" Never 'nawed a pig chucked yet, not aven weth dirt," grinned Aaron.

" Well, you shudn give un such big pieces, fer you knaw 'ee caan't clunk [swallow] 'em," she returned, more quietly, as we all saw there was no fear of Spottie's choking.

Sebudah might always be found " at home." Aaron went here and there, to market or fair ; but it was seldom he could induce Sebudah to go with him. Whether it was that she did not like the trouble of dressing up, or whether she really preferred staying at home among her household gods, I cannot say ; but I have a suspicion that it was the boot-cleaning, and the brushing and folding and putting away " the cloas " in the blue chest, which were the chief hindrances. These, and her saving propensities,

were, no doubt, the reasons why Aaron so
seldom wore his best clothes on a week-day.
He might often be seen at a funeral wearing a
pair of white fustian trousers, shrunken with
many washings, the legs coming about half-
way down a pair of Wellington boots, but given
a touch of "Sunday best" by an old grey cloth
coat and a high, rusty silk hat with a black
mourning-band. As he invariably stood near
the mourners, and bent over the grave to
see the last of the coffin, he was sufficiently
conspicuous.

In spite of Sebudah's stay-at-home proclivities,
she was once induced to go in the train. She
rode from one station to another—a matter of
ten or twelve miles. The speed in Cornwall is
not calculated to take your breath away, but
it had that effect on Sebudah. "Why," she
exclaimed, her face lit up with excitement, when
telling of the wonderful event, "we'd no zooner
got in the train 'nd I'd jist got mezelf comfortable, when the train stopped, 'nd we 'ad to git
out. I was never s' zorry in me life; fer, law,
they carriages was beautiful! I'll waage they
cost a purty penny. But, my graashus, we ded

go a purty coose; th' housen 'nd hadges [hedges]
was wuzzin' past jist like lightnin'—it fairly
maade me light-haaded. Aaron zaid 'ee'd like t'
ride t' 'Merica, but I doan't think I shud like
to go s' fur 's that." This was her first
and last experience of railway travelling.

She knew positively nothing of her own
county outside a twenty-mile radius; and, as
for holidays, I don't expect she ever had one
in her life. She was sometimes induced to go
to Summercourt Fair; but as she walked there
and back, and was in mortal fear all the time
lest she should have her pocket picked, or that
Aaron should buy something which they could
do without, I don't think it could rightly be
termed a holiday. Her sole aim in life was to
work and save for a rainy day; but, alas! when
the rainy day of old age overtook them, the
savings—what with the bad luck of the son
whom they had started in business, and the
breaking of a bank—had taken to themselves
wings, and the Union, which they had looked
at all their lives as the last resource of the
spendthrift, became their only refuge. What
they suffered before their poverty became

known can only be guessed at. When it was
whispered about that they could not pay their
rent (and that was their only debt), it was
concluded at once that they were penniless; for
to them debt and disgrace were synonymous
terms, and could only be incurred when starva-
tion was staring them in the face. I have often
wondered how the shock of finding themselves
in the despised "Union" affected them. The
fare, which to most people would seem so
meagre, would be to them almost luxurious;
and so, perhaps, there were compensations—
anyway, I like to hope so. But I wish I could
always have remembered them as spending their
last days among their household gods, comforted
by the caresses of Curley and the gambols of
"the Prenner."

CAP'N AND . . .
MISSUS TRELEAZE

South Terras uranium mine in the foreground and Terres tin mine top right, both close to St Stephen-in-Brannel.

IV

Cap'n and Missus Treleaze

WE were not much given in our village to tacking on titles to people except in derision. As a general rule, people were uncle and aunt, if they were favourites with the children, or plain John, Mary, or William, as the case might be, without any superfluities. But I never knew "Cap'n" Treleaze to be called by his Christian name. Sometimes he was spoken of as the "ould Terlaze," and occasionally, but not often, the older people called Mrs. Treleaze Sophia, but with the younger generation they were invariably "Cap'n" and "Missus" Treleaze. I think one reason for this was the Captain's assumption of superiority to the other inhabitants and his persistent aloofness, for he was never known to sit in anyone's house save his own. He also spoke much better English than the majority. Then, again, he kept the village store, was Captain at a local mine, and was reported to have a nice little sum in the bank; so that, taken all round, there was some excuse for his assumption, which was not often resented, but good-humouredly passed by.

Personally he was not liked, for he was pompous and overbearing, and had the reputation of being a bit of a slave-driver at the mine. He considered himself a very just man, but seldom showed mercy, and he was dead on weakness of any kind, physical or mental. If a man was ill, but for the sake of his wife and children came to the mine, hoping thus to secure his full month's pay, his hopes were thrown to the ground if the " Cap'n " found him out, and withering were the sarcasm and reproaches hurled at him. He was called dishonest and a sneak to come expecting to be paid for work which he could not do, and he was sent home, even if it were within an hour of leaving-off time, with the bitter consciousness that he had risked his health for nothing. If this came to Mrs. Treleaze's ears, she, good soul, would put an extra quantity of tea and a bag of biscuits in the basket when the wife or children came for the week's goods, for all the captain's employees were expected to deal at his shop.

I don't suppose it ever entered into the Captain's mind how completely in harmony with the primitive life and customs of the village his shop was. A large building with plate-glass windows and a lavish display of goods would have seemed not only ostentatious, but a blot on the picturesque reposefulness of the whole neighbourhood. Without knowing it, the Captain must have had an artistic soul, for his shop seemed simply a piece of natural evolution, and not something pitchforked into the place full grown. It was a low, linhay-roofed room, not more than six feet by ten, and had been added on to the back of his dwelling-house. It was only partly floored overhead, and this loft was reached by a ladder. Under the part that was floored, a man of medium height could not stand upright, but as men seldom came shopping that did not much matter. The amount of goods which they managed to store away in that little place was truly marvellous. To make your way from the door, which was in the end, to the one seat (a chair without a back) by the counter, you passed on your left the ladder before mentioned, a barrel of paraffin, a box of soap, a bag of dried peas, a stack of dried cod-fish, and a box of red herrings. On the counter, mingling their perfumes with the other conglomeration of smells, were a can of treacle, a tub of lard, and a few pieces of bacon. Rows of candles, brushes, boots, and tinware hung from the beams; and if you could steer your way safely without knocking any of these things down, you might consider yourself lucky. On the left wall over and behind the counter was the tea and dispensary department, the latter embracing such medicinal compounds as sweet spirits of nitre, castor oil, glycerine, and a red "drunch" (drench) for a cow. The groceries were kept in drawers in the counter and by the end wall opposite the door, where was also a small window, across which were nailed two or three narrow strips of wood

containing crooks, and on these were hung a few
penny cups for children and the small measures
used for hair-oil. Not very ornamental, it is
true; but as the window overlooked a garden,
and was scarcely seen from the road, no efforts
at display were made. Besides, everybody
knew it was a shop, so what would be the use
of dressing the window?

On the wall to your right were three shelves
and a narrow flap counter: this was the drapery
department. Here was a limited assortment of
calicoes, flannels, towels, and stockings, with a
few ounces of wool, and one or two cards of
needlework, or "embroadery," as Mrs. Treleaze
termed it. At the end by the door were kept
the salt-box and flour-barrel, with the large
scales and weights. Under the drapery shelves
and in all odd corners was an assortment of
" clome," cups and saucers, basins, dinner-plates,
jugs, and brown teapots, and a few earthenware
articles peculiar to our county—" putchers "
and " paddicks " (large and small pitchers), and
" stugs," deep round vessels used for pickling
meat and the winter supply of pilchards.

It was generally Mrs. Treleaze who attended

to the shop, the Captain's share in the business
being confined to keeping the books, making out
the bills, and balancing the accounts. On a few
rare occasions the Captain would be left alone,
and then, if customers came in, there would be
a bit of sport.

It was very strange, but as soon as it became
known (and what didn't we know?) that Mrs.
Treleaze was out, the neighbours suddenly discovered that they had run short of something
which they couldn't possibly do without. Then
would the Captain march into the shop humming
the nearest approach to a tune he ever managed,
with words of his own composing : " Tum, tum,
tum, tum," *ad infinitum*. If he managed to get
to the counter without knocking anything down,
the humming would go on until he got to the
tying up ; then it would cease, and he would
breathe hard instead. He could manage very
well if you wanted some big article ; but if you
wanted a " apeth " of pepper, or an ounce of
spice, or a drachm of " saffern," then the
Captain's big fingers were, as he said, " all
thumbs," and many were the papers and much
the twine he used to keep those parcels from

leaking. But suppose you wanted a quarter of a pound of candles, twenties, and they had got twisted round the nail behind the sixteens and eighteens, then dire was the confusion. In his efforts to disentangle them his head would come in contact with a string of pepper-boxes, which came clattering round his ears, or perhaps the handle of a saucepan would strike him in the eye; then the Captain's patience—never a very generous allowance—gave out entirely. Giving the candles a twitch, the string would snap, and the whole lot come to the ground. If Mrs. Treleaze happened to return at this time, the Captain took not the slightest notice of her, but as he picked out five whole candles from the wreckage and ran a piece of string through the wicks, he gave vent to his anger in the most withering sarcasm. According to him, women were fit for nothing but eating and drinking— they were too lazy to be tidy, and too idiotic to know what method was. If he had a boy of twelve at the mine who didn't know better than to hang things where no one could find them, he would dismiss him at a minute's notice. Mrs. Treleaze, in her quiet, good-humoured way,

5

would stand all his abuse until he spoke of
laziness ; then her ire would rise, and she would
tell him a few plain truths, much to the delight
of the audience. When it came to this, the
Captain would laugh sarcastically, and, with a
last parting shot, escape, very glad to leave the
confusion which he had created. As soon as the
door had closed on him, Mrs. Treleaze's rosy,
comely face threw off its vexation, and with a
little laugh she would remark, apologetically,
"Law, what a to-do there allays es when a man
'ave got to do anything. You mustn taake any
noatice of Willyum ; 'ee's sich a orderly man—
everything mus' be in its plaace, or else 'ee's
upset. Es there anything else I can git for
ee ? "

It was always the same : the Captain might
storm and rave in the most provoking way, and
on a few rare occasions she would retaliate, but
as soon as he was gone she made excuses for
him. Everybody knew that the Captain was
a good deal of a tyrant at home—interfering in
the smallest things, even to the kind of food
that should be cooked, what time his wife and
her sister (who lived with them) should go to

bed, and what clothes they should wear. But through it all Mrs. Treleaze kept her faith in him, and always spoke of him as " As good a 'usband as ever brathed." And then, perhaps, suspecting dissent, she would continue warmly, " Where will ee find a more upright, honest man than Willyum? 'Ee wudn't wrong anyone a farthin'; and as for a Chrestian, there esn't a man anywhere that raids his Bible more nor spends more time on 'es knees than Willyum do."

On Sundays there was nothing we children enjoyed more than walking home from chapel behind " Cap'n and Missus Terlaze." The Captain was a stout, broad-shouldered man, very sensitive to heat, and on a warm day we liked to see him take off his coat and carry it on his arm, his big, billowy shirt-sleeves catching the breeze as he walked. He had a way of squaring his shoulders, throwing out his legs, and planting his feet firmly on the ground which was to us very entertaining. While the Captain was as upright as a soldier—nay, as Sirree Nick once expressively told him, " Thee'rt more than upright; thee'rt an ould lie-back "—

Mrs. Treleaze, on the contrary, was rather bent, and took short, waddling steps. When, in imitation of the couple in front, Nipper, who was a little wizened boy, would turn up his jacket collar to represent Mrs. Treleaze's shawl, and, linking his arm in Snuffler's, a big, solemn-faced lad, who could take off the Captain down to the most minute detail, and the two walked solemnly behind the Captain and his wife, our enjoyment was complete, and we brought up the rear shaking with stifled laughter.

If the Captain did not look round, after a while Nipper and Snuffler would walk boldly ahead, while we closed up, waiting expectantly for the storm to break; and in this we were never disappointed. The more the Captain poured forth his wrath and disgust at what Mrs. Treleaze termed our "bouldashus impidence," the better we were pleased. We were sometimes a bit sorry for Mrs. Treleaze, for in our own way we were very fond of her; but then, why would she look so funny, holding on by the Captain's arm?

Spite of Nipper's delinquencies, he was "thicker," as we expressed it, with the Captain

than any of us. It was no uncommon sight, if
Snuffler was absent, to see Nipper march boldly
up to the Captain's side and commence a conversation. At first the great man would not
deign to reply, remembering past transgressions,
and also above joining in secular conversation on the Sabbath Day. But Nipper would
pave the way by discussing the sermon, and
telling some improving anecdotes about some
preachers he had heard in the west of Cornwall,
for he was not one of our parish. After this
he would start talking about the weather, and
how good it was for the garden. This would
interest the Captain, for he was an enthusiastic
gardener. Then Nipper would praise the Captain's crops, and tell some flattering speech
he had heard. By this time the ice had all
been thawed, and Nipper was restored to favour.
But sometimes the Captain was made to " eat his
own head," as we put it. I very well remember
the following conversation :

" Cap'n, you be a pious man, and very honest,
people do zay," Nipper began; "now, what
shud you zay ov a man that wud zell a poor
boay a pair ov shoes 'nd charge ten shelluns for

'em, and then in a month wan ov the 'eels comed clane off?"

"I should say he was a rogue," was the emphatic reply; for, as I have before said, the Captain had no mercy on other people's delinquencies.

"Simmen to me that's goin' ruther vur, edn ut, Cap'n?" Nipper asked, insinuatingly.

"Not a bit too far. A pair of boy's boots which cost ten shillings ought to wear for three months without requiring a stitch. You come to me, boy, when you want another pair of boots."

Ignoring this, Nipper continued: "Well, it ded seem ruther bad, fur I'm awnly a poor boay, as you knaw, Cap'n, 'nd I awnly git sixpence a day, 'nd faather es a crepple, 'nd what weth lodgin's up 'ere 'nd rent 'ome fer mawther, 'ee caan't avord to buy me a new pair. 'Twan't as ef I wared 'em 'ard, nuther. I was jist climmin' ovver a hadge and catched me 'eel in a brimble, 'nd off it come. Now I've got to ware me best boots to work in."

"Shame, a burning shame, I say, and the

man that sold them to you ought to be made
to give you another pair."

" Do 'ee raaly think so, Cap'n ? "

" Yes, certainly. I would do it if it were
my case."

" All right, then ; I'll come ovver to-morra
evenin', and you sh'll give me the new pair,"
announced Nipper, joyously, adding, as if by
an after-thought, " I buyed they shoes fr'm
Missus Terlaze a month ago."

The Captain's face was a study ; turning to
his wife, he stuttered, " Wha—wha—what is
this ? Is it true ? "

" I sould 'im a pair of boots, and gived you
the money ; but I don't expect 'ee's tellin' the
truth," answered Mrs. Treleaze, trying to speak
soothingly.

" Aw iss I be, 'nd I'll bring the shoes ovver
and shaw 'em to ee—you do knaw yer awn
boots, I s'pect ? "

Nipper did not get a new pair of boots (or
shoes, as he generally persisted in calling his
week-day gear), but he had the others thoroughly
repaired free of charge. And this was not all,
for he kept the story up his sleeve, so to

speak, bringing it out at the most inconvenient times, and always to suit his own purpose.

One Sunday we noticed that Nipper seemed quiet, not to say low-spirited; and though Snuffler was with us, and had strutted after the Captain in his own inimitable style, Nipper would not, in more senses than one, " catch on," and we were beginning to feel that the show was one-sided, when all at once the cloud lifted, an ingratiating smile settled on his face, and, leaving us without a word, Nipper walked up to the Captain, and said quietly, " Cap'n, I shud like to ask your 'pinion 'pon thickey verse the praicher rade to us 'bout Zaccheus. I've 'eerd that you knaw more 'bout the Bible than lots of th' praichers."

" Iss, that 'ee do," assented Mrs. Treleaze, proudly.

" What do you want to know about Zaccheus, boy ? " asked the Captain, condescendingly.

" Well, Zaccheus, by all accounts, wadn considered too respec'able ; but ef when 'ee chated people or ded any wrong restored fower-fowld, what ded convarted Chrestians ought to do ? "

The Captain was silent; it is possible that he remembered the boots, and suspected a trap; so Nipper continued: " What do you think 'bout it, Cap'n ? Ef a man comed to you and zaid he'd repented, and paid you back a pound he'd done you out of, wud you ax fer fower ? "

" Oh, no, certainly not; but you haven't got hold of the thing right. That was simply Zaccheus's method of justifying himself, but we aren't commanded to do likewise. You see——"

" I'm purten glad fer that," broke in Nipper, in tones of relief; and then, taking three pence out of his pocket, he gravely held them towards the Captain: " There you are then, Cap'n; 'twud 'ave scat [bankrupt] me ef you wanted the shellin'."

" What are you talking about? You don't owe me anything," said the Captain, in astonishment.

" No, but I spoase I've wronged ee, fer I cud 'ave 'ollered to ee when you was goin' to chapel, but I dedn't."

The Captain looked mystified, and Nipper explained: " Two chaps gived me threppence

not to tell you I zeed 'em ‚stailin' your gooseberries."

"What!" shouted the Captain, "my gooseberries that I was saving for the show? Why,
I took the first prize with them last year. And
you, you young rascal, saw them stolen?"

"You needn't be so mad with me, Cap'n; I
dedn taake 'em—I wuddn be s'mane; but I
dedn't think a few gooseberries was wuth much.
I've offered ee all they gived me, 'nd you zaid
yerself that we weren't commanded to restore
fower-fold; but ef nawthen else'll plaze ee,
'ere's tuppence more, and I'll pay ee the other
sevenpence as soon as I c'n saave et up."

The Captain pushed him on one side, and
strode home without another word, leaving
Mrs. Treleaze to follow without her usual
support.

Poor Nipper! I have often wondered since
if some dim presentiment of the future over-
shadowed him that day. The following week
some ground fell away, and almost buried the
little fellow. He was brought home to his lodgings, but there was little that could be done
for him. For several hours he lay unconscious;

but towards morning he opened his eyes, and
his landlady saw that his gaze was fixed on
his clothes, which were placed on a chair in the
corner. Thinking that he wanted something,
she brought them to him, and slowly went
through all the pockets. At last she came to
something wrapped in a paper. It was the
fivepence he had offered Captain Treleaze. As
she counted it out she heard him whisper, "I
caan't do it now." Then, seeing the troubled
look in his eyes, she took a shilling from
her purse, and placed it beside the coppers.
The trouble passed away, and his eyes seemed
to smile; then, making a great effort, he
gasped, "Shellin'—Cap'n Terlaze—fower-fowld."
And once more his eyes closed, but when
they opened again Nipper was "on the other
side."

When the woman told the Captain all this,
and offered him the shilling, he had to turn
away to hide his emotion. Some time after
that people began to notice that the Captain
was less hard than formerly; he seemed more
willing to forgive and less eager to condemn.
They said that age was mellowing him, but

Nipper's landlady always shook her head at such remarks. She had a rooted belief that the change was due in some unexplained way to "poor little Nipper," and the shilling which the Captain refused, and the "fower-fowld."

OUR . .
VILLAGE
ARTIST.

V

Our Village Artist

ES, we had a genuine artist in our village; and although he could not lay claim to those magic letters R.A. at the end of his name, nor had ever had a picture hung in the Academy, still he was not without claims to distinction. I well remember as a child pushing my way with a number of others into his workshop (I beg pardon, studio), a long linhay-roofed room built at the end of his cottage, to see his famous picture, " Mount Vesuvius in Flames."

It was my first introduction to the world of art; and after climbing on the carpenter's bench which was in the room, to bring myself on a level with the other people, I stared with all my might There stood the famous picture which

was to make the name of Joshua Endean great for
all time—the picture he had talked to everybody
about for weeks, but had religiously excluded
from all eyes until it was finished, and which he
now proudly unveiled before us.

It was a very large canvas, filling nearly
the end of the shop (oh dear ! studio). I have
seen many pictures since which have called
forth my warm admiration and made me break
the tenth commandment, but never have I
viewed a picture with such unqualified approval,
nor under quite such favourable circumstances.
My neck did not ache in the least looking at this
picture, for as I sat on the bench it was on a
level with my eyes ; neither did I have to consult
a catalogue to find out what the picture was
intended to represent, for here was a mountain
and no mistake, and here were the red flames
mingled with blackest smoke bursting up
from the top. At the sides also were little
spurts of flame, while around the bottom in
picturesque confusion lay a lot of dark-looking
objects, which the artist told us was the spent
lava.

"Looks jist like them clinkers you pull out

of your ingine, Billy," said Tommy Carkeek,
nudging a rather grimy-faced man near him.

" They do zay that thickey mountain 'ave bin
a burnin' ever since the world beginned, and
that it'll never stop. Who knaws?—p'r'aps the
bottomless pit es under that mountain," was
Billy's reply in awestricken tones.

" Well, you needn't be feared, Billy, When
you do pay a visit to the ould gent down below,
you'll be able to stand the vire better'n any
ov us," was the facetious remark of Jobber
Menhire.

" Doan't ee talk like that, Jobber my dear,"
said old Betty Pearce, plaintively. " Why, 'twas
awnly laast Sunday that the praicher was tellin'
us that he dreamed wan night 'ow he was
lookin' into the mouth ov 'ell. 'Twas jist like
a great ingine shaft, he said, awnly the sides was
all glass ; and as the vire flaamed and roared
and the smill ov the brimstoane 'scended up, it
made un quite sick 'nd faint. And as the devul
raaked the vire to make ut 'otter, he seed the
pore lost soals tryin' to climm up the sides ov
the shaft ; but who cud howld by 'ot glass ? But
some places 'twas cracked weth the het [heat],

6

and some on 'em got a good way up, and then
the devul reached up his raake and pulled um
down again.   And the praicher said the 'owls
they gived waked un, and the sweat was jist
rowlin' off un like pays—an' no wonder."

"That's a powerful tough taale, Betty," said
Jobber Menhire, with a humorous twist of his
wide mouth. "I expect thickey praicher ait
too much cowcumber and cowld pork avore he
went to bed, or else some cowld apple dumplins.
You c'n dream anything after they.   But we
dedn cum 'ere to talk about sarmons.   What be
ee goin' to do weth yer pictur now it's finished,
Joshua?"

"I shall send it to London to be exhibited;
then I shall make a present of it to the Queen,"
was the artist's reply, with a lordly sweep of his
hand, as though gifts to the Queen were of
every-day occurrence to him.   He was a little,
thin man, with light, silky, brown hair and a
pointed brown beard.   His features were good,
and there was considerable fire in his violet-
blue eyes.

Jobber Menhire pushed his battered billycock
a little farther back, and then, with a short,

forced cough, said, " Will she give ee anything
for et, do ee think ? She edn considered ovver-
generous."

" What does that matter ? It will bring me
fame, and that is all we artists live for," was the
magniloquent reply.

" A little ready money 'ud be 'andier 'nd
more acceptable to the people you do dale
weth, I reckon," said Jobber, significantly ; and
then he continued in his usual friendly tones,
" Ef I was you, Joshua, when I send the pectur
to 'er Majesty, I shud hint as 'ow you was
a pore man weth a fam'ly to keep. She's a
mawther 'erself, and she'll understand."

Whether Joshua acted on this hint, or whether
he ever found sufficient money to forward it
to the Queen, and what became of the picture,
I have no knowledge whatever. My memory
at that time was like a phonograph—it recorded
easily enough what was strongly impressed on
it, but to ask it for any connecting-links between
the records was quite useless.

The next recollection I have of Joshua was
after a visit he had paid to London. He was
so fired by the sights he had seen that he did

little for a week or two after his return but
go around among his old acquaintances to give
them a recital of the wonders he had witnessed.
Going to London twenty years ago was not
such a common thing as it is to-day. And
there were many then (as there still are now
in outlying districts) who had never been out
of their native county. Besides, Joshua was a
born *raconteur*, and he had no scruples whatever about painting a rose or gilding fine gold,
especially if the rose happened to be a little
faded or the gold begrimed with dust. Hence
it was that Joshua's descriptions of the places
and buildings he had seen in London were
listened to with the most absorbing interest.
Meals were as free to Joshua in those days as
the air he breathed, and in his off-hand, magnifi-
cent way he accepted them as freely as they
were offered. Nay, I think he considered them
his due, for he generally timed his visits when
meals were about.

As we listened to his vivid descriptions of the
National Gallery, the Houses of Parliament, the
Abbey and St. Paul's, of the theatres and
music-halls, public parks, and underground

railroads, London became for us the land of enchantment, and we looked forward to the time when we too should visit that wonderful city. Even a fog, as Joshua described it, was not without its mystery and glamour; and though to some of us a nearer acquaintance has shorn it of its glamour, it has lost none of its mystery.

How Joshua had managed to see so much in a fortnight, or where he had got the money to pay for all this sight-seeing, was something known only to himself. At home he was always poor and in debt. He did odd jobs of house-painting and carpentering, and in the summer-time he earned a few pounds by playing in the village band, at school treats, and other festive occasions, but of regular employment he had none. Every now and then he disappeared, leaving his wife and children to live as best they could.

Once, when he had been away for an unusually long time, and his family became chargeable to the parish, it was whispered about that Joshua had been heard of in Wales. This coming to the ears of the parish authorities, a search was made, and Joshua was discovered in a large country house near Monmouth. He was employed in the house as a decorative artist; and when the policeman came to arrest him, he was in the drawing-room, singing a plaintive love-song to the accompaniment of the piano. He had described himself as an artist on tour, and his suave manners, fluent tongue, and ready imagination had won for him a high place in the esteem of the owners of the house. So much were they taken with him that he was treated as a friend, and no objection was raised when it was known that he was paying his addresses to the governess. When he discovered the policeman in the room, he made no effort to escape; but, polite to the last, his only protest was, "For God's sake don't handcuff me before the ladies!"

When he appeared in court, and was confronted by his wife and eldest son, Claude Lorraine, his first exclamation was, "'Lizabeth, take him away to the tailor's, and order him a new suit of clothes at once. I can't have my son appearing in such rags."

"And I had only sixpence in the world," she plaintively told a neighbour afterwards.

I have a dim remembrance that he was sent
to prison for this escapade, but for how long
I do not know.   Anyway, when he was released,
his wife went to meet him, and received him
with open arms.   Albeit, as she lived in one
of the few poorhouses which our parish possessed, Joshua was very much distressed.   It
was such a terrible disgrace that he, an artist
who had been consorting with wealthy, refined
people, should have to live in a poorhouse.
He was so much upset about it that his poor
wife fell to apologising, feeling that in some
way the fault must be hers.   When they came
in front of the bare stone cottages and some
people were seen approaching, Joshua hastily
ordered his wife and children to leave him,
while he with head erect jauntily walked past
the houses as though he had never seen them.
A little later, when the people had passed and
no one was in sight, Joshua came back, and,
after looking once more before and behind him,
he made a sudden dart into the house, closing
and locking the door behind him.   And this,
the other inmates of the poorhouses said, was
his usual mode of entry while he remained there.

Joshua possessed more than the usual amount of pride ; but it was the pride that makes a person ashamed of only one thing—poverty. Poverty to him was a standing disgrace. He hated it as the devil is supposed to hate holy water, but he seldom let it weigh him down. Always jaunty, plausible, and picturesque, he skipped through life, and passed lightly over quagmires which would have engulfed a less optimistic character.

After his one great masterpiece, "Mount Vesuvius in Flames," I never heard of his painting another picture. He talked often about painting "Niagara in a Mist," but it never got started. He stuck to his music, however, sometimes walking five or six miles to sing at a concert, where he was always loudly cheered. He also sang in the church choir, and was a great favourite with the parson and his family.

Joshua was never above borrowing from anybody ; but he scorned the idea of charity ; and when his wife received coals and borrowed blankets from the charity club in the winter, Joshua was never supposed to know anything about it. However, once the parson broke

down this barrier, and politely hinted to Joshua
that, as the winter was now over, it was time
that the blankets should be returned.

Joshua professed to be very grieved that his
wife should have received such help, and spoke
of fortune as having been against him that
winter. Then, with a little deprecating cough,
he said that the blankets would have been
returned long ago, but the truth was that one
of the children had contracted a disagreeable
skin complaint, and he had really been afraid
to send them back, as the complaint was catching. The parson backed away immediately,
calling over his shoulder, "Keep them, Joshua—
keep them. Don't ever send them back."

By this polite little fiction Joshua procured a
couple of pairs of very nice blankets, without,
in his estimation, any loss of dignity. The
clever way in which he turned what to most
men would be intolerable positions into oppor-
tunities for self-display was almost ludicrous.

At one time the band was invited to enter the
lists in a contest. Joshua was a really good
musician, and the different members of the band
were well aware of his value. On this occasion,

however, Joshua utterly refused to go, on the
plea that he had nothing fit to wear. Here was
a quandary. To go without their best player
was to spoil their chances entirely. There were
many members of the band who could have lent
him a suit easily; but it was very well known
that Joshua had a weakness for appropriating
everything which came into his hands, and
people had grown shy of lending him anything
of value. At last, however, one of the members,
a big, good-natured fellow, seeing that nobody
else would come to the rescue, said that he
would lend Joshua a suit. It would be much
too large, but if Joshua kept in the background
it would not be noticed.

To do this, however, was utterly impossible
to a man of Joshua's temperament, and several
times during the day the other members of the
band were nearly convulsed to hear him swear-
ing at his tailor to everyone he spoke to—vow-
ing that though he had employed his present
tailor for years, and had paid him hundreds
of pounds, yet never again should he make
another suit of clothes for him, or see the
colour of his money again. The latter part

of this speech they had no difficulty whatever in believing.

Sometimes in the winter the band would be asked to play at a country-house ball; and on these occasions Joshua generally managed to get the ear of the master of the house, and hint to him that he was not a regular member of the band—that by profession he was an artist, but had consented to supply the place of a sick man, and looked at his evening's outing as a good frolic. His easy manners, gentlemanly appearance, and delicate hands bore out this statement; and while the other members of the band had supper with the servants, Joshua invariably had his with the guests.

Stories of his ready wit and unfailing resourcefulness were told by the villagers to every new-comer, while his witty sayings became household proverbs. Indeed, many a reputation for wit has been built up on an ability to recount well some of Joshua's numerous escapades, and to give point to a remark by one of Joshua's quaint sayings was as common as to speak. If a neighbour asked for a lift in a farmer's trap, he would be sure to remark as soon as he was

seated, " You know I am like Joshua Endean.
He used to say, ' When I pay my shilling and
ride in front of Ferrel's van, I sit *a ton*; but
when anyone offers me a lift, I sit as light as
a feather.' "

When Joshua grew older and his health
began to decline, his optimism and large belief
in himself seemed to fail him; and when he
ceased to astonish people by his daring, and
to amuse them by his wit, he fell into the
background, like any other spent force. Asthma
prevented him from playing in the band, and
completely destroyed his fine tenor voice. He
had by long years of ingratitude and selfishness
exhausted the patience and sympathy of his
friends; and when he was reduced to the much-
despised parish relief, most people thought it
was no more than he deserved. And, strangely
enough too, his wife, who had loved him through
all his neglect of her, and his many desertions,
now in her turn neglected him. It was pitiful,
but it was perhaps natural.

All through his life he had thought only of
himself: if after his wants were supplied any
fragments remained over, his wife and children

were welcome to them. To the pale-faced, drab,
slatternly woman, this gay Lothario, with his
optimistic nature, colossal conceit, and entire
belief in his own genius, was a never-failing
object of admiration and wonder, and in spite
of everything she was proud to be his wife.
But when all these attributes were stripped
from him by ill health, and he could not speak
without coughing, and sat all day long by the
fire, bent and withered, seldom speaking to her
except to snarl and complain, then she seemed
to grow tired, and openly spoke of him as a
useless burden on her hands.

The night before he died a bed-ridden neighbour in the room adjoining heard him begging
his wife to give him some water ; but she, tired
out with her day's washing, and half asleep,
told him to be quiet—that there was no water
in the house, and she wasn't going out in the
garden to draw water from the well at that time
of night—he must go to sleep and wait until
morning. All through his life he had never
spared her ; and now, no doubt unconsciously,
she had her revenge. For hours the neighbour
heard him moaning and begging at intervals

for water; then towards morning the moans ceased, and she fell asleep.

Joshua Endean had also fallen asleep, never to wake again in this world. After his death it was as though the last years of his life were blotted out, and people remembered him only as the gay Joshua who had cheated them often, broken all promises, and betrayed all trusts; but who, nevertheless, had provided them with an unfailing fund of amusement, and for this, though they would not have owned it, they admired him. During the last years of his life Joshua had died to the people, but with his death he lived again, and still lives. No tombstone, so far as I know, marks the grave of this great man; but none is needed, for the many stories of him will keep his memory green. There was one especially which was always told with great gusto; and as it illustrates not only Joshua's gastronomic greed, but his utter indifference to other people's comfort, and his ready faith in their willingness to supply his needs, I will give it here.

The story at first-hand had been told by *the* storekeeper of the neighbourhood. This man deserves a chapter to himself; for at a time when stores were rare, and when a five-pound note would have bought up the stock-in-trade of most village shopkeepers, he boasted, not without some show of reason, of being able to supply everything that was necessary for both man and beast. It was here also that people were relieved of the distraction of toothache by the still more painful process of extraction.

It was to this celebrated store, then, that Joshua wended his way one Monday morning in mid-winter at the early hour of four. The storekeeper was asleep, but was rudely awakened by a tremendous ringing of the bell. Thinking that only someone suffering the torments of toothache would disturb him at such an unseemly hour, he hurried shiveringly into his clothes, and ran downstairs, forceps in hand. As the bolts were shot back, and Joshua entered the shop, the storekeeper asked sympathetically, " Which tooth is it, Joshua ? "

" No tooth at all, Mr. Trethosa. The truth is, I haven't been able to sleep, thinking about what I should have for my breakfast; so just cut me a couple of nice streaky rashers,

Mr. Trethosa, and put them down to my little bill."

The almost speechless disgust of the store-keeper always varied according to the imagination and skill of the narrator, some going to the length of saying that he danced all round the shop in his stockings, while others pictured him pulling the hair from his head; but as he was bald, this was probably an exaggeration. But all were agreed as to the fact that Joshua not only had his bacon, but ate it.

FERREL'S
VAN . .

St. Stephens Square with a horse bus and the church in the background.

VI

Ferrel's Van

I DON'T think any description of our
old Cornish folk would be quite
complete without a description also
of the van in which they rode to
the weekly market. For the majority
of people this was the only mode of
conveyance, and on wet days even the farmers
often preferred to ride in the van rather than
in their own open traps. When the roads were
heavy, it took an hour and a half to do the five
miles; but at no time did Ferrel ever manage
to get up anything like speed. His two old
horses were as lean, wiry, and not-to-be-hurried-
looking as himself.

There was a joke that went the rounds that
the oldest passenger had never known Ferrel

or his horses young; but as both horses and master came from another parish, this could be explained.

Ferrel himself was a keen-eyed, ruddy-cheeked, dapper-looking man—his leather leggings and boots, always in a highly polished condition, giving him rather a smart appearance. He generally wore a long drab coat with big metal buttons, and a glazed sou'wester, in which get-up he seemed to defy all weathers.

He was rather a silent man, not at all given to gossip, although he must have listened to enough each week to fill a society newspaper. If he took any notice of the jeering and good-natured banter which was invariably indulged in about his horses' rate of speed, he did not let anyone know it. Uphill and on the level he kept up a continuous " Click, click, click " to the horses, presumably to incite them to more speed; but downhill, when the drag was on, and they broke into a trot because it was easier than to hold back, his face relaxed into a smile, and he looked complacently at the people he might pass on the way. This did not often happen; for it was the usual custom for

everything to pass him, though, by keeping in
the middle of the road, and pretending not to
hear the shouts from behind, he made this as
difficult for the other drivers as possible.

The van itself was particularly noticeable, the
top of it being painted a bright blue, and the
bottom a dark red. It was not a particularly
comfortable or commodious affair, in spite of
the fact that Mrs. Treleaze often remarked that
if it were possible she would " 'Ave luved to
ride to 'Merica in Ferrel's Van."

It would seat about eight people, not com-
fortably if they were full grown, for it was
very narrow ; but it often had to hold twelve
or fourteen. The people took all this squeezing
good-humouredly enough as a rule, for they all
had experience of how undesirable a five-mile
walk on a wet night could be. Many laughs,
and more groans, and several screams were
heard during the wedging-in and settling-down
process ; and when anyone got up to get out,
the sighs of relief were pointedly audible.

I think, however, that country people are
much less peevish and put about at the little
inconveniences of travelling than town dwellers.

Perhaps it is that the country people have a much larger fund of good humour to draw on, and are not so nervous and irritable. I remember once getting into a 'bus at Redruth, which was to convey me to Stythians. Stythians enjoys the unique position of being five miles from everywhere; and this being the case, that 'bus never lacks passengers. I had gone early to secure a seat, and before the time for starting came the 'bus was filled to overflowing. But we did not start any earlier, for there were all the baskets and packages to be stowed away on top. This top was nearly on our heads; so when the driver began stamping about and thumping parcels down, I began to feel rather nervous, lest he should come through. But nobody seemed to take any notice until after a thud which shook the whole 'bus, and covered us all with dust; then a woman in the corner rapped the top with her umbrella, and shouted in the sing-song tone peculiar to the west of Cornwall, "What art a-doin', then, Billy? Droppen' that pear of satinette slippers thour't takin' 'ome for tha wife?"

There was silence for a second or two, and

then I was startled by seeing a head hanging
over the side of the 'bus, and a pair of eyes
peering in at the window. " That thee, Grace
Martin ? " bawled the owner of the head.

" Iss, sure. Who else shud et be ? What
dost a-want ? "

" Aw, awnly to zay that when I do bring
'ome thy new sleppers I waan't carry any other
parcels—'twud be cruelty to the hosses. Aw,
aw, aw ! " Then the head disappeared, and
Billy " was quits."

There was a great deal of this kind of
pleasantry indulged in in Ferrel's Van ; but
nobody seemed to take offence at the broad,
outspoken remarks, though as a rule there
was seldom anything spiteful about them. A
countryman's idea of humour is not of that
subtle kind which needs a keen intellect to
grasp the point. He likes his jokes as he likes
his music—something that he can understand
and beat time to with his feet.

A subject once started, it was not allowed
to drop until everyone who wished to had
contributed his or her remarks. Humorous or
gruesome, religious or profane, there was no

help for it—the passengers had to listen until their journey ended. To do Jobber Menhire justice, however, when he was there the conversation was generally steered into tolerably safe channels; and being not only a humorous but an untiring talker, he assumed the position of unelected pilot without a dissentient voice. Sometimes, when he was in a musical mood, he would call for a song from some member of the company; but if some unasked person who had been indulging a trifle too freely started to sing a song which was not to Jobber Menhire's taste, he would bend his brows at the offender and say reprovingly, "Remember there are laadies present. Nawthing but sacred songs afore the laadies, I say." If after this rebuke no one was bold enough to begin, Jobber would sing his one and only sacred song, commencing, "Come, little cheldern, hearken onto me." After this cheerful ditty was over, Jobber would start the conversation rolling again.

There was one topic which seemed of never-failing interest to both old and young, and was a prime favourite of Jobber's, and that was love, or, as he termed it, "coortin'." Sometimes, if

there happened to be an old maid among the
passengers, the jokes, to an outsider, might
seem a little pointed; but as the victim seldom
ever showed that she felt it, the topic rolled on
merrily. If there should be an old bachelor
as well as an old maid in the van, Jobber
Menhire was at his best. Always polite and
careful not to offend anyone, yet in his good-
humoured, insinuating way he managed to say
all he wanted to without giving offence. For
instance, if Miss Curra, a tall, thin, sour-faced
spinster, was present, he would remark in a
concerned kind of tone, but with a sly twinkle
in his eyes which belied his words, " Now
doan't ee squeeze up aginst Miss Curra sa tight—
she edn used to et, yunnaw ; we ould married
wans, we doan't mind." Then, with a nod in
Miss Curra's direction, he would add, " You was
wise when you was young, Miss Curra, not to
be bothered weth a man ; now you'm saafe, and
can live out yer days in pace and quietness."
As Miss Curra was still not without preten-
sions to youth, it was doubtful whether this form
of consolation was particularly agreeable.

" What about Jan Crowle here then ?—mustn

he be squeezed nuther, 'cause 'ee edn married ? "
asked a stout, good-looking woman with a hearty
laugh, after one of these pleasantries.

As Jobber looked at poor, thin, attenuated
Jan Crowle pinned in between the speaker and
another woman equally stout, looking like a
hay-fork between two bundles of hay, Jobber's
chuckle deepened into a laugh as he remarked,
" Aw, never mind about Jan—'twaan't 'urt 'ee.
'Ee ought to 'ave 'ad a little more of ut 'ears
ago." And then, with a shake of his head and a
vain effort to look solemn, he continued, " But
there, marriage es a terrible lottery. No matter
'ow careful you may be in pickin' and chewsin',
you never knaw what you be goin' to git. What
I do zay es, 'tes like a muddy roade on a dark
night; 'tedn a bit of good pickin' yer way to kip
yer shoes clane, fer you caan't do it. You
might jist as well shet yer eyes and splash right
through."

" Why, Jobber, you're letting down the
women to liken them to mud," remarked a
smart looking young dandy, a budding school-
master.

" Nawthen' ov the sort, Mister Smith ; I

zaid marriage, and it taakes two to git married,
doan't it? No, no; there's nobody ever 'eard
me zay anything onkind about the wemmen; fer
I knaw that we men wud be wisht cratures
wethout 'em."

"Iss, iss, that we shud," assented Richard
Bluett, who was wedged in between Miss Curra
and a red-faced woman with her arms full of
parcels. "Ef my wumman edn in the house
when I go home, I hate to go inside the door,
and thats true. A house wethout a wumman
es like a pulpit wethout a praicher—no good to
anybody."

"Well, well, that depends 'pon the praicher,"
said Jobber, judicially. "I heeard ould
Granfer Pearce zay wance about a local
praicher, ' Why, a good *nawthen* ez better'n he.'
And I daresay there be zome men who wud be
glad of a empty 'ouse jist to 'ave a little p'ace."

Before anyone could reply Jobber continued,
"I daresay you moast ov ee knaw poor little
Edard Jose, as quiet a little man as ever brathed.
And yet I knaw, when he used to come 'ome from
his work in the ebnins, he used to creep up
to hes awn door like a thief. Then he wud

oppen et quietly and thraw in 'es 'at jist to zee what sooart ov a temper 'es wife was in. Ef she tucked up 'es 'at and 'anged it on the nail, he knawed he might come in; but ef she tuk et up and thrawd it out in the roade, the poor ould Edard used to wander around till she was gone to bed."

" Well, I think about as much of my wife as most men, but I shudn stand any tantrums ov that kind," snorted Richard Bluett, looking round the van and nodding his head emphatically.

" Well, I dunnaw; wemmen be tecklish craters to manage. You never knaw jist 'ow you'll find 'em, and what'll suit wan waan't suit another. Zum men do zay, maister 'em from the beginnin'; and others do zay, 'umour 'em; but my 'pinion es, howld 'em with a loose rein, but lave 'em knaw the rein 'es there."

" Phew! " said a bright-eyed little woman in the corner, contemptuously; " how you men do love to deceive yourselves! Place you behind a whirlwind, and put a pair of reins in your hands, and you would pride yourself on the fact that you were guiding it. Why, I don't suppose

there is a man in this van who would dare go
home and *order* his wife to do anything."

A rather shame-faced look crept over the faces
of the married men, all except Sam Jones, who
had been drowsing in the corner near the door,
but who now roused up at this challenge, and with
a beery kind of leer said, sententiously, " Some
ov us aan't got to order, Mrs. Basset—we aan't
got to wait fer that; they do things for us afore
they're asked. There's my wife, dear good sawl ;
she's just as 'appy as a duck ef she can awnly
'ave me 'ome. As soon as she can onlaace me
boots and git me in bed she's awl right, for she
say she knaw I'm saafe then."

" Your wife is a precious sight too good for
you, Sam," remarked a farmer, good-humouredly,
who sat next to him.

" Ded anybody ever 'ear me deny it ? Doan't
you think I doan't knaw what a good wife I've
got. She edn wan ov yer clever women like
Mrs. Basset auver there—I took good care not to
marry wan of they ; but as I allays zay, my wife
es a dear, aisy-goin' sawl, but she's wan ov the
best. The way that wumman do pray fer me es
wonderful ! When she do think I'm slapin', I

do 'ear 'er prayin' for 'er dear 'usband; and ef ever I do git to heaven, I shall knaw that 'tes because of the prayers she've offered up for me."

"You doan't calculate there's much chance of your gettin' there on your own 'ook then, Sam?" asked Jobber, jocosely.

" 'Bout as good a chance as yours, Jobber," was the quick retort. " I git drunk sometimes, I knaw, and I zay and do things that baan't as they shud be; but I doan't oil the coaats ov ould cows and file their 'orns to maake them look young, and zay 'tes their eighth caaf when 'tes their eighteenth."

There was a general laugh at this, while for once Jobber seemed to have no reply ready; and Sam continued with maudlin gravity, " No, no, Jobber, ould man; you and me'll boath 'ave to turn awver a new leaf afore we die; and may the Lord 'ave mercy 'pon us!"

" Sam is always 'specially religious when he's half-seas over," said the farmer near him, sarcastically.

" And doan't I need it moast then? You be a Churchman, Maister Penhale, and zo be I; but

my wife, she's a chapel wumman, and she do zay
we must all repent and be converted before we
be fit to die, and she's prayin' all the time for a
revival."

Sam relapsed into a doze for a few seconds;
and then rousing himself up and looking around
at the others, while a smile spread over his
broad, good-looking face, he asked, " Ded I
ever tell ee 'ow I nearly started a revival
myself wance? Well, my dears, 'twas like
this : The local praicher that was praichin'
at our chapel got catched in a heavy storm of
rain as he was comin', and he was wet through;
but there wadn't time to go anywhere to be
dried, so he stayed and praiched in they wet
cloas ; consequently, when he comed to our 'ouse,
hes teeth was knackin' in hes head, and he cudn
touch a bit ov dinner. I maade un drink a
doase of brandy right there and then, and I
zaid to my wife, ' You go and warm our bed
right down hot, and put on another blanket,'
and I towld the maid to put on zome milk to
boil, and they ded ; and when he was in bed, I
took up a big cup of 'ot milk, with a naation
good doase of rum in it; but he dedn knaw that,

and I towld un to drink it right off, and he'd be all right in a hour or two. Well, my dears, he ded as he was towld, and slaped like a top till taytime. Then, weth his cloas dried, and a good tay inside 'im, he was like a new man. When my wife comed 'ome from chapel in the evenin', she said he had praiched like a man inspired, and she was sure the time was ripe for a revival. 'That was the rum, my dear,' I zaid. 'Ef I'd awnly gived un another glass afore he went, you'd 'ave 'ad the revival to-night.'"

"The first time I heard Sam tell that story 'twas only one glass—now it's two; next time I expect it will be three," remarked Mr. Penhale, drily.

But Sam's head had dropped again, and he was dozing once more. The doze lasted until the van stopped for him and one or two others to get off. Before he left he came again to the door, and politely begged our pardon if he had said anything that was wrong, and then with a little lurch walked away towards the Queen's Head, where he would befuzzle his poor brain with a little more spirits before he took it home to his waiting wife. Alas, poor soul! she had need to be " aisy-goin'."

FERREL'S
VAN . .
CONTINUED

VII

Ferrel's Van *(continued)*

T was a cold, wet, blustering night; and though the steamy smell of wet clothes is as a rule very disagreeable, yet after the rain, wind, and mud of the streets the stuffy warmth of Ferrel's Van was almost comforting, and the passengers, after pushing as many of their baskets and parcels under the seats as possible, settled down to their hour-and-half's journey with something very like a sigh of content. It had been a disagreeable day since early morning, and so only those who were obliged to go to market had ventured out. Although it was the kind of night which made the taking of an extra glass of grog quite excusable, even in the minds of those who sometimes needed an excuse for such indulgence, yet everyone was perfectly sober. But what was stranger still was the entire lack of the bantering pleasantries which were usually indulged in.

Something was amiss evidently, for even Jobber Menhire added nothing to his polite "Evenin', laadies," as he entered, while Sam Jones's rollicking, good-humoured face looked as near doleful as such a ruddy countenance could. At last Jobber broke the silence by saying, "Terrible thing about poor old Jonathan Rickard, edn et? They be zayin' that he must 'ave 'owld up hes feet weth 'is 'ands to 'ang hisself, fer the stittle [head-stall] was that short 'twas a wonder 'ow he cud 'ave done it."

There was no need for Jobber to explain himself; everyone in the van had heard how Jonathan Rickard (once a well-to-do farmer, but latterly doing little but lounging around the public-houses) had been found that morning hanging from a stall in a cattle-house, where he had been conveyed the previous night by the landlord of the King's Arms, and shut up there to sleep off his drunken stupor. It was

generally supposed that when he had come to
his senses in the early dawn, and realised the
indignity which had been placed on him to be
housed with the cattle, shame and remorse had
so preyed on his mind that he determined to
put an end to his existence.

" 'Twas a unhuman thing to do," said Sam
Jones, in tones of solemn and weighty displeasure.
" Jist because the poor fella had a wakeness fer
drink, and dedn knaw when ta stop, 'twas a
mane thing to tie un to a stittle, jist as though
he was a dumb baste. I 'ope the curriner'll give
landlord Bell a good reprymand."

" Aw, there edn no doubt 'bout that. But
awnly think what a terrible wisht thing it'll be
for hes pore wife, to zee un lyin' there cowld
and stiff in the tower. I spoase Bell wudn 'ave
un brought into the public, so they 'ad to taake
un into the tower. They'll take un into the
church porch as zoon as he's put in 'is coffin,
I 'ear," said Jobber, with a kind of gloomy
relish for all these details.

" Well, I'm no believer in ghoasts ; but, all the
saame, I shudn much like 'avin' to go in that
belfry to ring the bell these dark nights, that I

shudn," said Richard Bluett, with several defiant
nods.

"That waan't effect Billy Southey, you may
depend. He's too much accustomed to diggin'
graaves and pickin' up boanes to mind there
beein' a corpse in the belfry. 'Twud taake a
good dale to frighten ould Billy." A smile
struggled around the corners of Jobber's wide
mouth as he spoke; and then, looking round the
van, the old twinkle came back to his eyes as he
continued, " They do zay as 'ow ould Billy used
to sell the boanes he picked up from the graaves
to the rag-and-boane man, and that his wife got
quite a nice set of chaney and lots of clome* that
way. But the passon got wind of it zome'ow,
and he comed down on Billy like a clap ov
thunder, and ordered that all boanes vound
shud be berrid again, so that there shud be
no danger of their gittin' into onconsecrated
ground. They zay that Billy nearly lost 'is job
ovver that business, the passon was so mad
about et. He praiched a sarmon 'bout sacker-
lidge the next Sunday, and everybody knawed
'twas to Billy ; but law, I dunnaw ef the devul

* Earthenware.

hisself cud frighten a graave-digger. They do
zay that Billy doan't believe there es a devul,
awnly he waan't awn up to et, fer fear the passon
shud turn un off."

"Well, ef he doan't repent, 'e'll find there's
a devul saafe enuff when he do die," said Sam
Jones, with an ominous shake of his head. "Fer
my pairt, I doan't believe in talkin' so aisy about
the devul; he edn wan to maake a mock of, I
zay, for we are towld that ' he goeth about
like a roarin' lion, seekin' whom he may devour.'
There was Aaron Jinkin, *he* knawed there was a
devul when he tried to 'ang 'isself, for he zaid
there was allays a voice at 'is elbow tellin' 'im
to make 'way weth 'isself, and wance he nearly
done it. Hes wife found un curled up under a
gooseberry bush weth a rope 'round 'is neck,
black in the faace, and nearly dead. When he
comed to, he zaid that as soon as ever he putt
the rope round 'is neck somethin' pulled et
tight, and he knawed 'twas the devul. No,
no, 'tedn no jokin' matter."

The smile departed from Jobber's face, and
his jaw dropped slightly, making him look aged
and careworn. Then a woman who had been

fiercely nodding her head, as if in approval of
Sam Jones's remarks, now burst out, " You
be 'bout right there, Mr. Jones, and there
be they as wud maake jokes at their awn
mawther's graaves ef it waan't fer shame ov
what people wud zay; but they doan't joke when
they do come to die—they be feared enuff then.
There was the caase of that infidel up at St.
Dinny's, who died two 'ears ago ; they zay the
devul comed for 'im afore he was dead. He
was screechin' and 'ollerin', and zayin' he was
burnin', till the people who was settin' up with
'im dedn knaw 'ow to stay in the room, they
were that frightened. 'Twas 'ushed up a good
dale, for the saake ov 'is poor wife ; but this
I do knaw, for the carpenter that maade the
coffin towld my brother with 'is awn mouth."

Here Mrs. Tregony's teeth snapped together,
and she looked around at her audience, no
doubt to see the effect. The look of strained
interest on some of the faces must have been
very gratifying, and, lowering her voice, she continued still more impressively, " He said that,
when he comed into the room to missure the
corpse, everything looked jist as if there 'ad been

a vire. The bed, the planchin' [floor], and the corpse hisself was swimmen' weth water. He zaid he 'oped he would never 'ave to maake a coffin for a infidel again."

" Oh, come, come, that story must be terribly exaggerated, Mrs. Tregony," said Mr. Penhale, a little impatiently. " I expect the truth of the matter was, that the poor fellow was suffering from some fever, and said he was burning hot, and the ignorant people who were sitting up with him, knowing he was an infidel, put an entirely wrong construction on the whole affair. Helped to kill the poor fellow probably by pouring buckets of water over him."

Mrs. Tregony threw out her hands and opened her mouth in horrified dismay at such deplorable scepticism, and then, pursing up her mouth, she said sternly, " We are towld that there be *some* people who wudn believe even though wan rised from the dead."

The look of surprise which spread over Mr. Penhale's face was too comical for Mrs. Basset's gravity, and she burst into a hearty fit of laughter ; and though she must have known that most of the others were looking at her with stern disapproval, this only seemed to make her the more powerless to stop.

Jobber Menhire, after one or two visible efforts to escape the contagion, allowed his features to relax, and with a little apologetic nod around at the others said coaxingly, " Well, well, 'tedn no crime to laff, anyway, and we was gitten' terruble gloomy. We be all in the land of the livin', and that's somethin' to be thenkful for, I taake it; so let's be cheerful, and, as the song do zay, ' drave dull care away.' Now then, Jan Crowle, turn up the conders of yer mouth, and look a little more as ef you was goin' to be marrid instid of goin' to be berrid. Why, gor jay, we might all be in a 'earse instid of bein' in Ferrel's blue-and-rid van. Give us a song, Jan ; you aan't brok your voice jawin' yer wife and zingin' yer cheldern to slape, like zome ov us 'ave. Doan't be shy now ; do zummin' to shaw people that you'm alive."

Always ready to take a rise out of an old bachelor, the gloom lightened, and there was a general look of interest turned in Jan Crowle's direction. Poor Jan's large, cadaverous face, with the long locks of coarse black hair hanging

round it, lost something of its corpse-like aspect
at Jobber's pleasantries, and at last a broad grin
spread over his face, showing his long yellow
teeth.

" That's right, Jan; 'owld yer 'ead up and
oppen yer mouth wide, like the primmy-donnas
that my son do talk about. Now, doan't try to
look sa modest, fer I've 'eard as 'ow you used
to play the tromboane in the chapel wance."

Jan coughed slightly, and then said in his
soft, drawling voice, " Well, I did for a little
while; but 'twas my brother William as
you've 'eard about, I expect. He was a
famous player."

" Iss, iss, they was good times in the ould days,
afore 'armoniums was ever 'eeard of," said
Richard Bluett, regretfully. " I can mind the
time when I used to walk miles to Sca'cewater
chapel jist to 'ear the music. Why, 'twas good
awnly to 'ear 'em tunin' up their fiddles before
the sarvice beginned. There was three fiddles,
a baaze vile, a tromboane, and wan or two
flutes and a piccolaw. I shall never forgit
wan Sunday arternoon; they played ' The great
archangel's trump shall sound ' to the tune of

Job, and when all the people joined in 'twas a wonder it dedn rise the ruff [roof]."

" Aw, but ef you thought the music grand then, what will et be when we git up above, where there is a multitude which no man can number ?—" Ten thousand times ten thousand, and thousands of thousands, singin' the praises of the Lamb that was slain."

This outburst came from a little old woman who was covered from her throat to her feet with a thick cloth cloak, gathered into a yoke and fastened with big bronze clasps. Her face, which was the colour of old ivory, was one network of wrinkles, and was framed by a gathered hood of the same cloth as her cape. This was Betsy Nicholls, who, though it wanted yet a month to Christmas, had already begun her rounds to collect her Christmas presents. Alone in the world, and in receipt of parish pay, she was pitied by many generous-hearted farmers' wives, and numerous were the pieces of bacon, half-pounds of butter, loaves of cake, and eggs which found their way into Betsy's large bag, well covered up by her ancient cloak.

Intensely religious after a peculiar fashion of

her own, and much given to quoting Scripture,
Betsy was known to go off into a kind of
religious frenzy after talking about the glories
of heaven ; and at such times she would jump
and shout in a way that might prove very
disconcerting in such cramped quarters as
Ferrel's Van. She was seated opposite Jobber
Menhire; and as he caught sight of the rapt,
fixed look which was now settling on her face,
he began to shuffle his feet and appear uneasy.
How to head her off was evidently the idea in
Jobber's mind, for the next minute he leaned
forward and said mysteriously, " 'Ave 'ee 'eeard
'ow Solomon Juleff's Jersey cow es bewitched ?
Zome ov the neighbours be zayin' that 'tes
Betsy Floyd as 'ave done et, because 'ee dedn
pay 'er enuff when she cured 'is oss that
'ad the rounders. But Solly do 'cuse poor
liddle Jemima Jolly. He do zay that she 'ave
cast the evul eye 'pon 'im because 'ee dedn
marry 'er darter ; but that she caan't 'urt 'ee
because he was borned on a Sunday when
the moon was vull, and 'es father and granfer
was seventh sons. 'Owsever, Solomon es in a
terrible to-do about et ; they do zay 'ee's like

a man maazed, fer the cow was the finest he
'ad on the plaace."

Jobber had saved the situation, for even
Betsy Nicholls was not proof against the absorbing interest of witchcraft. Besides, witchcraft was, so to speak, a Biblical subject, and
therefore not unprofitable for discussion. Now,
though some of the younger generation at this
time were beginning to make scoffing remarks
about witches and ill-wishing, and disbelieved
in charms and tokens, the majority of the older
people had never a doubt about such things
being true. They cited instances of cows
having been stung by adders, when nothing had
been done for them save repeating a charm, and
the cows had recovered. Then there was the
well-known case of the boy who had shot off
his thumb, and was in danger of bleeding to
death before the doctor, who lived five miles
away, could be fetched; but a neighbour who
knew a charm for stopping blood had been
called in, and the bleeding had ceased. When
the doctor arrived in great haste, she had said
to him, quite as a matter of course, " It's all
right, sir ; I've charmed his hand, and the blood

have stopped." The doctor had stared at her,
and asked angrily, " Do you set yourself up as
God Almighty, that you pretend to be able to
stop blood by the saying of a few silly words ? "
And the woman had answered meekly, " No, sir ;
but I can stop it by using His name, as you can
see for yourself." The man of science had no
reply to make to this, and the power of charms
was considered more than ever irrefutable.

And so it was that, when Jobber Menhire
started the subject of witchcraft, nearly everyone had something to say on the subject.
Richard Bluett and Sam Jones had had cows
charmed for adder stings, and never troubled
to send for a farrier ; while two of the women
knew cases where " kennons " (cataracts) in
the eyes and many ringworms had been cured
by charms.

" I baan't no disbilaver in charms fer anything
'cept toothaache ; and the awnly charm fer that
es cowld steel," summed up Jobber, humorously.
" I mind wance I 'ad et for a week, and I was
nearly maazed. I zaid ovver and ovver again
thickey charm fer toothaache, which p'r'aps zome
of ee knaw. It do run like this : ' As Peter

set by the gaates of Jerusylem a-weepin', a angel
comed to 'im and zaid, " Why weepest thou ? "
and Peter said, " Because I be sorely afflicted
with the toothaache." And the angel said, "Weep
no more, for henceforth whosoever shall keep
these words in memory, print, or writin' shall
nevermore be afflicted with the toothaache." ' "

" Powerful words, Jobber; I wonder if it was
intended for a rhyme ? " asked Mr. Penhale,
drily.

" I'm sure I doan't knaw; but, anyway, it
dedn cure my tooth."

" Well, what did you do ?—learn another
charm ? "

Jobber wiped his mouth with the back of
his hand; and then, rolling his large protrud-
ing eyes round at the passengers, he broke
into a low chuckle as he replied, " 'Twadn
much of a charm, as you shall 'ear; but
it settled me tooth. We dedn knaw nawthen
about daintists in those days—the blacksmith
ded the job fer us then. I do offen tell my
maid that 'tes a pleasure to 'ave a tooth
pulled now, and wuth 'aaf a crown awnly to
zet in the grand chair they do give ee.

'Owsomedever, as I was a-zayin', I was nearly
maazed, and, though 'twas laate Saturday night,
I tramped off to Edart Trudgeon's shop ; but, just
like my luck, Edart wadn 'ome. His mawther
zaid that Ambrose was in bed, and she'd call'm
ef I liked. You zee, the ould wumman dedn
want to lost the sixpence. I axed ef Ambrose
cud pull teeth, and she zaid that 'ee never 'ad,
but she dedn zee why 'ee shudn, fer 'ee was
stronger in the arms than Edart. Well, just
then my tooth give such a haive that I nearly
hollered, so I zaid I was willin' fer anybody
to 'ave a try at the villain. To maake a long
story short, Ambrose comed down, and we went
out to the shop. They 'adn any of those new-
fashioned things they do call forceups (naation
good naame fer 'em too, I zay)—awnly the ould
crook. Well, Ambrose putt the crook round my
tooth, and tried un ; but 'ee slepped—'twas too
big. Zo 'ee in wed'n in the vire, which 'adn gone
out, and then bal'd [beat] un down, and tried
un on me tooth ; but 'twas no go. ' Putt'n in
again, Ambrose,' says I. And 'a ded, and bal'd
un down wance more, and this time 'twas small
enough. By golly ! the ould wumman was right

9

when she zaid that Ambrose was stronger than Edart; fer 'ee not awnly pulled out me tooth, but 'ee brok out a great piece ov me jaw as well. That's why I aan't never bin aable to talk very well never sence.''

There was a good deal of laughter over the wind-up of Jobber's yarn, and some wonderment was expressed as to what Jobber's powers of speech would have been like had he the whole of his jaw.

" Well, never mind; I've maade ee all laff, my dears; and 'tes 'ealthier to laff than to cry any day—that's my 'pinion. There, Ferrel es pullin' up: who'd 'ave thought we was so near Churchtown? Well, I wish ee all good-night, and a merry Christmas when it do come.''

OUR . . .
PRACTICAL
JOKER . .

VIII

Our Practical Joker

NEARLY every village has its "fools" and its "practical jokers," and ours was rich in both. But the king of the practical jokers was, without doubt, "Ould Barnicoat," as he was always designated. Now, as I try to recall this quaint old character, I am led to ask myself with considerable surprise whether I ever met this old man in the flesh or whether I only knew him from hearsay, and I cannot answer. It may be that I saw him when I was a child, or, again, he may have been dead years before I was born. And yet I have the feeling that I must have known him perfectly well, although I cannot recall a single meeting. All the same, I have a perfectly clear mental picture of the tall, thin, flaxen-haired, rather dried-up old man, with weak, watery eyes, and red-rimmed lids; but whether this is only a description oft repeated, or a mental photograph, I am again in doubt. But his name was such a household word, and the tales of him were so numerous, that an entire stranger could not have lived long in our midst without feeling that he knew "Ould Barnicoat."

By trade he was a carpenter, and many were the practical jokes he played on Rab Harvey, his assistant, in the carrying out of that business. I may as well state here that in Cornwall most country carpenters are also undertakers, the making of coffins being the most remunerative part of their trade. In the carrying out of his practical jokes, Barnicoat did not seem to allow any doubts about the truthfulness or the honesty of his proceedings to stand in his way; but, at the same time, there was nothing " underhand " about him; he made no secret of the fact that on moonlight nights, when he and Rab were kept up all night making a coffin, they used to go to a neighbour's orchard, when it was the apple season, fill the box with apples, and bring

them home for future consumption—for, as he
would remark with great glee in his high-
pitched, squeaky voice, "Nobody will stop a
man with a coffin to see what's inside."

He used to be fond of recounting also how
he one night persuaded Rab to go to a certain
smith's shop where were two bags of potatoes,
one of which he was to bring home, as they
were very short of potatoes, and must have some
for to-morrow's dinner. (He took care not to
tell Rab that he had bought the potatoes that
day.) Away went Rab, who seemed to think
that he had not to "reason why," and away
also went Barnicoat by a shorter route. By the
time Rab reached the blacksmith's shop Barnicoat was already there hidden underneath the
great bellows. When Rab laid his hand on one
of the bags, he was startled by hearing a most
terrific groan. Rab, who was terribly super-
stitious, was, as he afterwards told Barnicoat,
"Frightened moast to death ; my teeth fairly
knacked together." But standing in some fear
of his master, and ashamed to go back empty-
handed, he resolutely caught up the bag and
turned to leave, when his ears were assailed

with a string of groans so terrible that he threw
down the potatoes and bolted out of the shop,
running for home as fast as his one lame leg
would allow.   When Rab returned to the
carpenter's shop, breathless, and with his eyes
almost starting from his head, Barnicoat was
also there, breathless too, and shaking with
laughter, so that his voice, when he spoke, was
almost a shriek.

"Where be the tetties?" asked Barnicoat.

"Aw, maister," groaned Rab, his fears in-
creasing at these signs of anger, as he considered
them, "doan't ee zend me back again, maister—
doan't ee ; fer I caan't go.   The devul es there
behind the billeys, and 'ee wudn lave me tich
the tetties."

"Well, never mind, Rab," said Barnicoat,
soothingly; "the devul es good to tha arter all,
fer he've brought the tetties 'ome fer tha."   And
there against the wall, sure enough, to Rab's
great astonishment, stood the bag of potatoes.
In winding up this story Barnicoat always
added, "And I do believe that Rab 'ave 'ad a
sort of sneakin' kindness fer the ould devul ever
since."

Another one of Barnicoat's jokes was to go to Mr. Trethosa's shop when he knew that worthy was away, and ask the old lady, his mother, for a " pound of gimlets." Mrs. Trethosa, in all good faith, took down the box of gimlets, and then remembered that she could not weigh them, her son having that day taken away the weights to have them tried. " Never mind," squeaked Barnicoat, " my hand weighs exactly a pound."

Never doubting this statement, Barnicoat was allowed to put his hand on the one scale, while the old lady poured the gimlets into the other ; but there were not enough to make up the pound, according to Barnicoat's weighing.

" Never mind, my dear ; I'll taake thewse I've got, and 'ave the others when the maister gits in a new stock. I allays pay sixpence a pound fer my gimlets " ; and he gravely tendered the sixpence. To do the old man justice, it must be stated that he returned all the gimlets save two that same evening to Mr. Trethosa.

One of Barnicoat's practical jokes, however, was said to have caused quite a scandal in the parish. In old Parson Rawlin's time, before

the church could boast of an organ, the singing was accompanied by different kinds of
musical instruments. These instruments were
sometimes left in the vestry. Now, Barnicoat,
having been called in on the Saturday to do
some repairs, seeing the large bass instrument,
could not resist the temptation of rolling up
some shavings and pushing them into the
cavity. As ill luck would have it, old Nathan
Thomas had a habit of blowing softly into
this instrument, to see that it was all right, while
the parson and congregation were reciting the
Belief. Sometimes the instrument had been
known to emit a soft note, much to the parson's
disgust; but, like most musicians, Nathan was
rather touchy, and so the parson bore it in
silence. On the morning after Barnicoat's visit
to the church, Nathan, blowing into his beloved
instrument to see if it was all right, quickly
found that something was amiss. He turned it
upside-down and shook it; then blew again.
Still something was wrong. He began to
blow harder and harder, in his excitement
forgetting his surroundings entirely, until, with
his face red with exertion, he took a long,

deep breath, and blew with all his might ; the shavings flew out, and with them a mighty blast that startled the whole church. The parson and the majority of the people were shocked and scandalised, but Barnicoat and a few other light-minded folk rolled on their seats and shook with helpless laughter.

Another of Barnicoat's escapades was in connexion with an exciseman. In those days the excise officers were anything but favourites. It happened that Barnicoat and a few others had assembled at a public-house to hold their annual club feast ; and just before the dinner was served an excise officer rode up to the public-house and ordered some supper. But everybody being busy over the unwonted bustle of a club dinner, he was told that he must wait. Being tired and hungry, he made his way to the kitchen, perhaps with the intention of hurrying on his supper, or, more likely, being drawn by the appetising smell of roast beef. Only the servant-girl was in the kitchen at the time— the landlord being engaged in drawing the ale, and the landlady in seeing that everything was just right on the dining-table. The beef was

on a large dish ready to be carried in, and the
girl was bending over the gravy on the stove.
The sight and smell of the beef were too much
for the hungry exciseman, and, taking up a
knife, he neatly carved himself a slice, turning
the joint over that it should not be seen. But,
as ill luck would have it, old Barnicoat had
also been drawn towards the kitchen to see
how the dinner was progressing, and witnessed
the theft. Without a word to the exciseman
he returned to the dining-room; but when the
beef was brought in, he took care to turn the
joint over and tell the others what he had seen.
The men were furious at the liberty which
had been taken, and one or two of the more
pugilistic kind wanted to "go" for the exciseman at once. But Barnicoat insisted that it
was foolish to spoil a good dinner even to
punish an exciseman, and advised them to
have their dinner first and take their revenge
afterwards.

"Never fight when you'm leary, fer yer heart
waan't be in yer work; besides, wan full sack
is wuth a dozen empty wans," was Barnicoat's
sage advice.

As soon as supper was over, Barnicoat sketched
the mode of attack. Three would be sufficient
for the job—one to " drub " the exciseman, as
he put it, and the other two to act as umpires
and see fair play, for the exciseman was to be
challenged and given a chance of defending
himself in the ordinary way. Barnicoat and
Rab were to be the umpires ; while Fat Jack—
so called because he looked like a walking
skeleton—was to do the " drubbing." Now, as
Fat Jack, though looking more like a corpse
than a living man, had once been a prize
wrestler and something of a pugilist, he was
not such a mean antagonist as he looked. It
was possible, too, that shrewd old Barnicoat,
having an eye to the after-effects, had chosen
him as much for his looks as his pugilistic skill.
There was a story told of Fat Jack, who was
also a carpenter, that once, when putting a corpse
in the coffin, which, owing to a mistake, had
been made rather narrow, one of the arms flew
up and struck Jack in the face. Incensed at
this treatment, Jack spat on his hands, and,
putting himself in position, cried out, " Come
on then, Billy Udy ; I was never 'fraid of ee

when you was livin', and I baan't goin' to be
now you'm dead."

But to return. What happened to the exciseman that night came out at the next sitting
of the magistrates, when Barnicoat and his
confederates were summoned for assaulting an
exciseman. Solicitor for the plaintiff described
how his client, going home one night from the
exercise of his lawful duty, was set on by three
ruffians, made to get off his horse, and, when he
showed fight—for his client was a brave man—he
was assailed by a perfect giant, against whom
his client had no chance whatever. After this
he was ducked in the horse-pond, dusted all over
with flour, and then, blindfolded, was tied on his
horse, with his face to the animal's tail, and led
through the village to the diabolical music of
sundry tin pans and much hooting and derision.

Barnicoat conducted the defence in person;
and, according to all accounts, it ran something
after this fashion.

"Your 'onour's warshup, we be three poor
working-men who caan't afford to hire anybody
to tell lies for us, so I be selected to tell your
'onour the truth. You've bin towld all about

a little joke we played on the exciseman; but
he've took good care not to tell ee why we
done it. It was like this, yer 'onour : We belong
to a little club, and every 'ear we 'ave a bit ov
dinner and spend a pleasant evenin' together.
Some ov us, yer 'onour, be so poor that we
'ardly taste a bit of beef except at this dinner,
and, nacherly, we look for'ard to it a good deal.
Well, yer 'onour, we was all gathered together
waitin' for our dinner to be brought in ; but—
would you believe it, sir ?—when the round of
beef, which 'ad been bought by our 'ardly
earned shellens, was putt upon the taable, some
ov us was for goin' out wethout taastin' it—not
because we wadn 'ungry (for noane ov us 'ad
'ad any tay), but because our feelin's was too
much for us. That exciseman there, who calls
hisself a gentleman, had been into the kitchen
and 'elped 'isself to our beef; and 'ed a-hacked
it about so that you'd 'ave thought that a cry of
'ounds had been benangling it. If he'd a-come
like a man and asked for some denner, we'd 'a'
shared it willingly ; for though we be poor,
we baan't greedy. But no, he was too much
of a gentleman to ask, but not enough of a

gentleman to keep from stalin'. And then, yer 'onour, as he'd sarved us such a trick and spoiled our bit ov dinner, we thought we'd sarve 'im a little trick—and I for wan caan't say I'm sorry."

" I understand he was terribly punished by one of your men. Which of you was it ? " asked the magistrate.

With that Fat Jack rose and showed his corpse-like face and skeleton frame ; and after a deep, hollow cough, which he could produce at will, said in a melancholy voice, " I be the fightin' man, your honour."

The contrast between this pitiful-looking skeleton and the strong red-faced exciseman was too much for the magistrate's gravity, while the crowd burst into roars of laughter.

The upshot of it was that Barnicoat and his men were let off with a small fine and a caution not to take justice into their own hands again, while the exciseman had to pay his own costs and bear the hoots and derision of the crowd.

On one side of his nature " Ould Barnicoat " could never have grown up ; for in the carrying out of his practical jokes he was as conscience-

less and indifferent to other people's feelings as
a mischievous schoolboy. But, spite of this,
he was not by any means an ill-disposed man,
for he was known to do many a kindly deed,
and he no doubt felt a very genuine fondness
for all children and animals. He seldom met a
group of children without stopping to talk to
them, and put them through a sort of catechism.
From their answers he would predict what
would be their future careers. Sometimes, however, the old man's love of mischief would prove
too strong for his affections. Thus, in meeting
a couple of small boys going to the mine with
their father's dinner, he stopped them and took
the basket, saying that he was hungry, and
must have the dinner. In telling the story to
the boys' mother, the old man said gleefully,
"The ouldest boy wud 'ave let me keep the
denner without a struggle, jist because I said I
was hungry; but the little wan, he laid 'owld
of the basket and kicked me, and cried in such a
passion, 'You shan't 'ave my da's dinner,' till I
had to give up the basket, or he'd 'a' kicked my
legs black and blue. He'll make a famous soldier
when he graws up, fer 'ee'll fight agin all odds."

10

At another time, passing by a cowshed which was near the road, and hearing voices, the old man was delighted to discover what was evidently a boys' prayer-meeting. A big revival had broken out at the chapel during the previous week, and the boys were evidently filled with the sincerest form of flattery. Looking through a hole in the door, Barnicoat saw three boys kneeling on the straw, and one of them was praying with considerable fluency; the other two were groaning and murmuring "Amens." This went on until the speaker, after a short pause, shouted fervently, "Lord, send down the influence," when one of the boys growled out, "Giss on, you fool—wot's thee knaw about influence?"

"I nearly doubled up weth laffin'," was the old man's comment in telling this story. "That boy ought to be a judge when he graws up, fer he 'edn goin' to be taken in by no flummery."

In religious matters Barnicoat was something of a free-lance; he girded at both church- and chapel-goers with equal impartiality, and pointed out their many shortcomings as faithfully as any parish priest. By all accounts these exhortations were anything but well received; and once, after telling a group of Sunday-school teachers that they " 'adn't more religion among the lot of them than a fly cud carr' in 'is eye and not feel oncomfortable," one of the group, a rather sanctimonious old bachelor, burst out heatedly, " I'm not a betting man, but I wouldn't be afraid to bet five pounds that there isn't a man in this parish that enjoys more religion than I do."

" Ee, ee, ee!" laughed Barnicoat, delightedly— " that's it; you've 'it the nail on the 'ead this time Religion and money, 'tes allays naation cloase together in yer minds—as cloase as the sarmon and the collection, and tedn offen you git wan without the other."

Barnicoat's own religious beliefs would be hard to define. He evidently believed in a future life, and also in a judge who would be lenient towards all mankind. Once, after hearing the fervent belief expressed that a place had been prepared in heaven for every true believer, Barnicoat announced with rather irritating satisfaction that he would get a better place than any of them.

Asked his reasons for such an astonishing
assertion, he who was a member of neither
church nor chapel, the old man replied, " That's
just where I shall bate all you fellas. It'll be
something like this, I reckon. Saint Peter, he'll
be sittin' at the gate, and he'll ask everybody
who they belong to. Wan'll zay, ' Church of
England ' ; then he'll zay, ' You go there—that's
your party.' And another'll zay, ' Wesleyan,'
and another ' Primitive,' and another ' Bryanite,'
and he'll tell everywan to set weth his awn
party. Then I shall come along, and Peter'll
zay, ' Who do you belong to, then, Barnicoat ? '
and I shall zay, ' I doan't belong to anybody ' ;
and he'll zay, ' All right, Barnicoat—you go just
where you like ' ; and I shall pick a good sate,
I can tell ee."

It may have been that underneath this fancy
sketch lay the old man's serious belief in a
universal heaven. And who shall say that this
belief was any more unreasonable than many a
narrower creed by which men have lived and
died ?

Searching my memory, I can find no record
of Barnicoat's death, and so have come to the

conclusion that the old man must have put his belief to the test ere ever I drew breath, which is only another proof how strongly he had impressed his personality on the memories of his survivors. People of Barnicoat's type do not die in country places—they are only translated.

CORNISH
REVIVALS

Family home of the Hockings in the late nineteenth century at Terras

IX

Cornish Revivals

N evangelist once complained to me that he was greatly disappointed with the results of his labours in Cornwall. He had been given to understand that Cornish people were very excitable, quickly moved to laughter or tears, and intensely religious; but, instead, he had found them quite the reverse. They had listened dry-eyed to stories which had moved other audiences to floods of tears, while his passionate invitation to them to " leave the ranks of the sinners and come out on the Lord's side " had been utterly disregarded. He had told stories of death-bed scenes which were enough to make the most callous tremble, but they were not even impressed.

I could have told him that his stories, com-
pared with the ones we had been accustomed to
hear all our lives, would have about the same
effect as a story of a bloodless raid on a boy
who had followed the fortunes of Umslopogaas.
But I contented myself with quoting the old
copy-book proverb, "Too much familiarity
breeds contempt." I wondered, however, what
he would have thought, could he have come into
our chapel a year or two earlier, in the midst
of a revival which had arisen at a time when
no one was thinking about it, and no special
services were being held. It seemed to have
nothing to do with the preacher either, for he
was an ordinary local brother, mournful and
rather prosy. But a young girl, who had
resisted all the eloquence of a series of "re-
vivalists," who had coolly argued with and
questioned all those who had come to talk to
her during the special services, and had at last
been given up in despair as a second Pharaoh—
this young girl had decided to become a Church
member, and, knowing of only one way—that of
the penitent-form—had got up in the middle of
the last prayer and knelt down under the pulpit.

At such a time in the late spring it would have caused excitement had it been one of the most hopeful of cases; but when this apparently impervious young person quietly left her seat and walked to the front, it caused a thrill of excitement to pass through the place seldom known in the village. It was the beginning of such a revival as had never been witnessed in that chapel since it was built. The singing-pew was given up wholly to the penitents, and the choir sat where they could. It did not matter, however; revival hymns were started from all parts of the chapel. People who, at any other time, would have been nervous at raising a tune, now thought nothing of it. And everyone seemed to find a voice. And such singing! No one who has ever heard the singing at a Cornish revival ever forgets it. It was at the time when mining was brisk in our neighbourhood, and a number of men from the west of the county were lodging in the place. Hearing of the revival, all the first and night " core " men had turned out. And what voices they had! Tenor, treble, or bass, they seemed to be able to sing any part that was needed most. Some of them could read music, the majority probably could not; but I never heard them make a discordant note. Working underground is, in many cases, a dangerous and unhealthy calling, but it develops the most beautiful voices; and as only hymns are ever sung underground in my county the rendering is perfect.

I remember once, when coming up from Penzance, that at Camborne a number of young men came tumbling into the railway carriage where I sat with two other ladies. They were a boisterous party—laughing, cracking jokes, and singing. Some of them had probably had a glass or two more than was good for them, or it might have been only animal spirits; but the two ladies who sat opposite me began to look very frightened, and I heard one whisper nervously, "Oh, I do wish we could get out!" But the train was in motion, and there was no chance. Seeing at the first glance that they were young miners in their holiday clothes, going into Redruth, probably for the Saturday evening market, I leaned across and said with a smile, "It's all

right; they are Cornish miners. You needn't
be a bit afraid."

It was during that terrible time when so
many men were buried alive at Dolcoath Mine;
and addressing a merry, curly haired young
fellow, who seemed to be indulgently looking
on instead of participating in the rather rough
play, I asked if he had heard if any more men
had been found that day. The others must also
have caught the purport of my question; for
immediately a sad look spread over all their
faces, songs were hushed, and then they told me
they had all been to the mine to know the latest
news. They eagerly gave me particulars of
the accident, each one adding his quota to the
general remarks, and giving personal reminis-
cences of narrow escapes they had had. And
then the one whom I had addressed, as though
to explain their conduct, said, " It's awful
whisht, miss; but we git used to thoose things,
just as our eyes git used to seeing in the dark.
We never knaw whose turn it may be next, so
it aren't no use grievin'. It's our livin', and
we've got to put up with it." And then, as
though anxious to change the subject, he turned

to another, and said, " Strike up, Bill " ; and
" Bill," without hesitation or delay, started in a
clear, beautiful tenor voice a hymn that is often
sung at funerals in Cornwall :

> Thee we adore, eternal name,
>   And humbly own to Thee,
> How feeble is our mortal frame,
>   What dying worms we be.
>
> Our wasting lives grow shorter still,
>   As days and months increase ;
> And every beating pulse we tell
>   Leaves but the number less.

The tune was a rare old Cornish tune,
doubling the last two lines of each verse. They
took up the four parts ; and our carriage, that
had been full of noise, was now full of melody.
Who could have believed, looking at their
grave, earnest young faces, that they were the
same rollicking crew who had entered the
carriage a little while before ? And yet, when
we stopped at Carn Brea, and some more of their
comrades joined them, some standing up and
some sitting on the others' knees, all their
solemnity had gone, and I was not sorry when
they got out at Redruth and we had breathing-
space once more. Yes, the evangelist was not

misinformed when he was told that we were an impressionable race ; but the gift of understanding is not given to all.

But I have wandered away from my subject. I need hardly say that to an onlooker there were many things done in a revival which would seem not only peculiar, but very mirth-provoking. It was not at all an unusual thing to hear two men commence to pray in different parts of the chapel at the same time, and, covered by a running accompaniment of " Amens " and " Praise the Lords," neither of them become aware of the fact. Then, again, if a prayer-leader dropped his voice, someone, perhaps, who had been talking to the penitents, thinking the prayer finished, would start a hymn, and everybody would join in, for we were always ready to sing at such times ; and the interrupted prayer-leader never seemed to mind, joining in as heartily as any.

Of course, we heard some very peculiar prayers, for there are always people who like to hear their own voice, and during revival services was the only chance some of them got. There was one young giant, whose strength had

all gone into the physical man, leaving the
mental in the background entirely. His prayers
were something unique in their very grotesque-
ness. He started off one night at the top of
his voice, "O Lord, we thank Thee that Thine
arm is not shortened that Thou canst not hear."
It was not often, however, that his friends
allowed him to hold forth—they knew his weakness, and guarded against it. Then there was
another man whose prayers were composed
almost entirely of passages of Scripture and
verses of hymns, with just a few words of
his own as connecting-links ; and whenever he
prayed a little black-eyed man, who sat up in
a corner (he reminded me of the little Japanese
men and women on my mother's tea-box),
invariably accompanied him, sometimes repeating the whole of the last line, but laying
great emphasis on the last word. As the man
who prayed had a high-toned, sing-song voice,
and the little man a deep bass, the effect was
very comical. My brother and I used to take
off the two for the amusement of our friends.
He, having a better memory than I had, sus-
tained the chief part, but I always managed,

when I could not remember more, to come in strong on the last word.

There were things done, too, in revivals that looked irreverent, but they were not meant to be. I have heard my mother speak of a woman at the penitent-form who seemed to be in great distress, when she suddenly ceased weeping, took off her shoes (a new pair) to see if she were bending them at the toes, and then, probably satisfied by the inspection, began to weep again.

To anyone not versed in the ways of Methodism, a Cornish revival would seem a peculiar, almost an uncanny thing. For weeks it is the chief subject of conversation. You seem to breathe it in the atmosphere, you see it on people's faces, and you feel its influence everywhere. The farm lads sing revival hymns in the fields as they follow the plough, and the millers' boys as they drive along the roads in their carts. You hear snatches of melody from the cottages as the women move about their work, and every evening the darkness is made vocal by bands of youths and maidens singing revival hymns as they go or come from the

11

services. Even the little children at their play are imbued with the same spirit. It is very sweet and almost pathetic to hear those little mites giving expression to sentiments which, if rightly understood and really believed in, would make the stoutest heart quail. I remember once being struck by hearing a little four-year-old girl singing, oh ! so sweetly :

> Oh, won't you be tonverted, tonverted ?
> Oh, won't you be tonverted while you may ?
> Turn, poor sinner, and 'stape 'ternal fire.

Looking up at me, she said, gleefully, " My daddy's tonverted. Mammy says we'll all doe to heaven togedder now."

At the chapel you are conscious of the beaming smiles of satisfaction on the faces of the prayer-leaders, and the look of eager expectancy on the faces of the ordinarily indifferent members of the congregation. The prayers are no longer characterised by the spirit of a wrestling Jacob, but are rather outpourings of thanksgiving for blessings received and for those yet to come.

With a good many this strong faith dies away when the revival ends, but with others it dies

only with their death. Through great troubles
and many afflictions they have been known to
say with Job, "Though He slay me, yet will I
trust in Him."

As one grows older and life becomes more
complicated, and doubts assail one's childhood's
beliefs, and faith is more a something to long
and strive for than an inherited possession, one
is led to wonder if there is anything more in
revivals than a restless desire for change, and
a love of excitement. And yet we cannot get
over the fact that many are truly "born again"
in revivals, whose changed lives are an eloquent
testimony to the genuineness of their conver-
sion. One especially comes to my memory as I
write ; for, next to my father, I admired him
more than any man in Cornwall. He was one
of the few Christians who always seemed to live
in the sunshine. It may have been a question
of temperament—I cannot say, though I have no
doubt that he had his dark days—but I never
remember seeing him without a smile on his
face. His was a little, wizened, plain face, as
far as features and colouring went, but made
almost beautiful by the expression and a pair of

sunny blue eyes, as liquid and clear as a baby's.
I never saw him at any gathering without feeling an added brightness, and, no matter what I
was doing, I always managed, sooner or later,
to get somewhere near, so that I could hear him
talk.   And when a year ago I received a letter
telling of his death and read the newspaper
cutting giving a description of how, in over-
looking some work, a piece of ground had fallen
and crushed him so that he never regained
consciousness, I felt as though some of the sunshine had gone out of the world for ever.

His was a life all too short; his work was left
unfinished; but, perhaps, it was none the less
effective for that.   Someone has said that to
the Christian sudden death means sudden glory.
Be that as it may, the influence of such a life
does not end with death.   I like to think that
death was robbed of its terrors for him, that he
merely stepped off the dusty highway of life,
and, as an old Cornishman quaintly put it,
" Took a short-cut home to heaven across the
fields."

SOME . . . . .
CORNISH . . . .
CHARACTERISTICS

X

Some Cornish Characteristics

IF a prize were offered for the most attentive, patient, and least restless listener to sermons, speeches, and lectures, I certainly think it would be unhesitatingly awarded to the Cornish Methodist. He will patiently sit out the lengthiest and prosiest sermon, and it is of the rarest occurrence for anyone to get up and leave the chapel before the sermon is ended. I never remember but one preacher being audibly interrupted, and I have always thought there was a legitimate excuse for the interruption.

It was a bitterly cold afternoon in December. The snow lay thick on the ground outside, and an east wind was blowing which seemed to find its way everywhere. We had no means of warming our chapel, and as the time passed on

we grew colder and colder.   Not so the preacher ;
he seemed to be warmed by his own eloquence.
We commenced the service at 2.30, and at a
quarter to four he had only got about midway
in the explanation of his text.   I was beginning
to wonder if some of us would be able to cover
our two miles' walk, get our tea, and be back
for the evening service, when we were all
electrified by a voice at the back of the chapel
saying, calmly, " Time to give out a hymn now,
brother."   Never before nor since have I seen
such a rapid close to a service which promised
to be endless.

As a rule, however, Cornish people thoroughly
enjoy a good sermon; but it must not be dry—
that is a deadly fault.   Let a preacher get a
reputation for being " dry " and " long-winded,"
and his chances of a large congregation are nil.
He will find that only a few of the " faithful "
will come out to listen to him.   All the same,
Cornish Wesleyans are the most loyal people
I have ever met.   They will always find something good to say of their minister.   If he
should be neither " very learned," nor " clever,"
nor " an easy speaker," then he is a " good man "

or " not a bit proud." If they cannot find a
positive virtue, there will be always a negative
one to fall back upon. Some of the other
Methodists, however, are not so loyal, and a
joke that tells against the minister, as long as it
is a good-natured one, is much relished and
often repeated.

I remember one story which was told me of a
young and zealous minister who was trying to
exhort an old and hardened sinner to repent-
ance; and when all argument and entreaty had
seemingly failed, he wound up his remarks by
saying that he should not cease to pray for him.
Then, seeing the old man's incredulous smile, he
added, impressively, " Yes, I shall pray for you,
and you know that

> The devil trembles when he sees
> The weakest saint upon his knees."

" Well, I doan't wonder at ut, fer I've heeard
some on 'em pray dree-quarters of a hour solid.
But say, maister, ef you do want to give the
devul a pill that even 'ee caan't clunk [swallow],
jist you ask un to come and 'ear ee prache."

*   *   *   *   *

Although fond of an argument, the ordinary Cornishman, in my estimation, is not a good debater. Flashes of wit, bursts of eloquence, quaint and picturesque language, often characterise his speech ; but, as a rule, he cannot stand what a Londoner would term " heckling." To have his most carefully thought out sentences met with smiling derision, his facts questioned and put to naught, his passionate eloquence received with cold silence, is more than he can bear calmly ; hence it is that Cornwall has sent out so many more preachers than politicians. But he has a nimble wit, and often scores a point by the use of it. Sometimes (but this is a failing not alone peculiar to Cornishmen) he will wriggle out of a tight corner by a bit of personal experience ; and this, though it may not be argument, is often very disconcerting to an opponent. This was so in the case of a young sceptic who was insisting to an old farmer that good could not come out of evil.

"But I knaw it can," was the triumphant reply. "Wance, when I 'ad inflammashun in me eyes and dedn 'ardly knaw 'ow to bear the pain, I went to the public-'ouse and got drunk.

Comin' 'ome, I falled awver a great 'eap ov stoanes and cut me eyes all to pieces. But it took away awl the inflammashun; so what wud you call that but good comin' out of evil?"

*　　*　　*　　*　　*

There is no one who loves a humorous, well-told story better than a Cornishman. It does not matter even if the story tells against him; if it is kindly done, he will enjoy it. But once let him think (if you are a stranger) that you are laughing at him, and he will withdraw himself inside his shell as completely as a snail when its horns are touched. With his own countrymen, however, he will hit back without mercy. This reminds me of a story I heard only a short time ago of two men who were both rather afflicted. One had had his nose broken by the kick of a horse, and the other had lost an ear. They both spoke broad Cornish. It was New Year's Eve; and as they passed each other on the road, the one with the defective nose sang out cheerily:

"'Appy New 'ear to ee, matey."

"'Appy new noase to you," was the snappish reply.

Cornish people have the reputation for being very hospitable, and, on the other hand, very 'near,' where money is concerned. This is not much to be wondered at, when it is taken into account that fifteen shillings a week is the general wage among labourers, while with farmers, although there is always food in abundance, money is generally a scarce article. There was a saying in our parish that the day after Lord ——'s agents had taken away the annual rents, you might comb the parish with a fine-tooth comb and not find a shilling. Be that as it may, the saying that you can get anything from a Cornishman but his money is not so very far wrong. People generally value most what they have least of. I have known a farmer chaffer for two hours over a sixpence, and then, if he succeeded in getting it, inviting his opponent indoors and giving him a dinner which he could not buy in London for four times that amount. Money is a commodity which has to be worked very hard for, and only to be parted with when nothing else will serve; therefore it behoves the purchaser to keep his "weather" eye open and see that he receives full value for his money.

The thrifty trait would probably account for the hesitancy of a young man who came to his friend to ask for advice. He said he had saved ten pounds, and he didn't know which it would be best to do—to get married or buy a bicycle. The friend advised him to buy the bicycle, for the reason that it would not cost anything to keep. This was a very conclusive argument, and the advice was followed.

Thrift is such a strong characteristic of the Cornish character that men, and women too, often work long years after they should legitimately be resting. Many old men work up to within a few days of their death. Indeed, when it is remarked that an old man is unable to go to his work, the news is generally received with a shake of the head and the remark, " Poor old man ! he won't be long now." In the summer-time men of sixty will walk sometimes three miles to their work, toil eight hours, walk home again, and then cut furze or trim hedges to earn a little extra. Every cottager has a garden, with which he supplies his family with vege-tables, and many take another piece of ground

to grow sufficient potatoes to keep their families
and the inevitable pig through the winter. If
they should get a day off to go to a fair or the
seaside, they invariably do double work the day
before. There is not much smoking done, and
to be drunk is considered a disgrace, something
which the women of the family do their best
to hush up and to hide. Sometimes, however,
thrift overcomes shame, and the man is held up
to ridicule. This was the case of an old man
who, happening to pass the public-house on a
very hot day, thought he would indulge in
a glass of beer. The landlord, seeing him
coming, said to some others, "Here's an old
Methoday—now we'll have some fun." What
was put in the beer I cannot say; but when
the poor old man came into the air again,
his legs gave way, and he fell along in a heap.
A wheel-barrow was procured, and he was
taken home, and was ill all night. The next
day a neighbour, calling, was surprised to see
him at home, and asked if anything was the
matter. He replied, with a groan, that he
was very ill.

"Ill!" echoed his wife, sharply. "He's been

drunk." Indescribable emphasis on the last
word.

"Aw, do ee 'owld yer tongue; I do veel
s'bad."

"Sarve ee right for gitten drunk." Then to
the neighbour, " I wuddn't care 'ow much 'ee
suffered ef 'ee 'adn't lost 'is day's work."

   *   *   *   *   *

Methodism in Cornwall is very strong; and
this is not to be wondered at, for in the outlying country districts the chapel provides the
only source of interest and amusement. This
last may sound rather a strong word to use ; but
I know that we used to extract a great deal of
fun out of our entertainments, concerts, and
teas. I can imagine that this was not always
so, and that in the early days of Cornish
Methodism the thought of amusement in connexion with the Church would be considered
little better than a device of the evil one.
Something of that feeling still lingers among
the older ones, for I remember as a young
girl being much perturbed by hearing a local
preacher holding up the reading of fiction as
a special sin to be shunned. He spoke so

eloquently, and quoted with such thrilling effect
that verse commencing,

> No room for mirth or trifling here,
> Or worldly hope or worldly fear,
> If life so soon be gone,

that I, who was much given to devouring everything in the shape of print that came in my
way, felt very conscience-stricken, and forswore
novels for some weeks. As I think of the
severity with which that sermon was delivered,
I cannot help wondering what the sermons were
like fifty years earlier. Even yet I have a
sneaking feeling of sympathy for the old man
I have heard my mother speak of, who always
insisted that he hadn't time to attend to religion,
but would wait until he was ill. When that
day came, he still put it off, until at last one
morning, after the doctor had left, seeing his
wife in tears, he asked her what he had said.

"Why, 'ee do zay you be mortifyin', Jan."

"Aw, mortifyin', be I? Then 'tes time to
zee about et. You may zend for th' passon
now, Mally."

But those days of ignorance are past, and
now nearly everyone is connected with the

church or chapel either directly or indirectly ;
for if the parents only turn out when some
special preacher is announced, they regularly
send their children to Sunday school, and so a
link is formed. Rank unbelief is but seldom
met with, and doubts on theological subjects
are not common—at least they were not a few
years ago. I used to think that our religion
had a good deal of the " Only believe and you
shall be saved and yours is Christ for ever " ring
about it ; and that our ready faith in God
arose more from a shrinking from responsibility,
and a desire to throw it all on the Creator, than
from a rational belief in the goodness and mercy
of God—in short, that our faith was more a
matter of custom and instinct than of thought
and reason. But lately I begin to think differ-
ently. I can see now that people who live close
to Nature, who are all their lives surrounded by
natural forces, forces untouched by man's in-
genuity, are naturally more impressed by a belief
in the power behind all these forces—a power
which they have no hesitation in calling God.
God is all around them, near to them. They
fear Him in the mighty storms which dash

12

vessels to pieces on their rock-bound coast, and bless Him in the gentle rain which makes their crops grow. But mostly they believe in Him when they sing. Then it is that the Celtic nature comes uppermost. Hard times and ambition for wealth are forgotten, and they revel in their one luxury, which has cost them nothing—the luxury of song. True it is that Cornwall can boast of no nightingales, but she abounds in singing birds. What can be sweeter than a country hedgerow in June, covered with dog-roses and honeysuckle? What it lacks in cultivation it makes up in profusion. And so it is with the Cornish voices. Cornwall may not produce many queens of song, but a man or woman who cannot sing at all is a *rara avis*.

Sometimes, when I grow a little tired of the flat, tuneless voices of the " Cockneys on their native 'eath," I close my eyes and dream that I am down in old Cornwall, with the smell of the salt sea mingled with the perfume of dog-roses and new-mown hay all around me ; and gathered together to hear some famous preacher is a great crowd, and among them are Cornish miners—miners from South Africa, Colorado, and California—and they all join in singing their favourite hymn :

> O God, our help in ages past,
>   Our hope for years to come,
> Our shelter from the stormy blast,
>   And our eternal home ;
>
> . . . . . .
>
> Time, like an ever-rolling stream,
>   Bears all its sons away ;
> They fly forgotten, as a dream
>   Dies at the opening day.

And as I listen to their clear, beautiful voices, I forget that emotions do not make morals, that singing hymns does not prevent people from driving hard bargains, that the doctrine " Blessed are the poor " is not so much thought of as " Ask, and it shall be given you."

My eyes are closed, and for the time I am blind to the faults which so often mar the character of " we Cornish."